T/C£375

2.50

Essays on
Probability and Statistics

Essays on
Probability and Statistics

M. S. BARTLETT, F.R.S.

Professor of Statistics,
University College, London

LONDON: METHUEN & CO LTD

 BARNES & NOBLE, Inc., New York

Publishers · Booksellers · Since 1873

First published 1962
Reprinted 1964
1–2
© *1962 M. S. Bartlett*
Printed in Great Britain
by William Clowes & Sons Ltd
London & Beccles
Cat. No. 2/6488/11

Contents

CONTENTS

Preface

Survey articles and lectures usually receive scanty attention from reviewers and abstracters, being dismissed as expository, or even without comment at all. Yet among the welter of new research contributions much represents temporary and even useless activity, which a little more general reflection might have avoided. Moreover, there is not often much opportunity to indicate one's general philosophy and outlook in research papers. I have consequently risked collecting together the present set of lectures, given by invitation since the last war in various places, in the hope that out of an apparently somewhat miscellaneous bag a unity and coherence of statistical theory, wherever applied, will emerge.

Many of these lectures have already been published in journals, and I am most grateful to the Editors and publishers in such instances for permission to reprint. As a rule (any exceptions to which are noted; for example, one or two added footnotes are put within square brackets) no alteration to the published draft has been made, for I believe that these articles stand the test of time reasonably well and while there is certainly nothing sacrosanct about the actual texts it is best to reproduce them in their original form. The reader is, however, requested to bear in mind their dates of publication. The set is not exhaustive; for example, my paper on 'The statistical approach to time-series', given at the Symposium on Information Theory in London in 1950, has been omitted because much of the material in it was in 1953 incorporated in my book on *Stochastic Processes*.

Of the last three articles (which have not previously been published), the final one comes in a somewhat different category, being the substance of a short talk given in an informal Manchester University lecture series on the philosophy and methods of science. A scheme to publish this series fell through, and the written version I had prepared with such publication in mind seemed worth including in the present collection as an elementary but relevant commentary on the controversial problem of statistical inference as I view it. Here, however, I subsequently added an Appendix containing some further remarks for the more sophisticated reader, as in this way the relation of my article to recent publications on statistical inference should become clearer, and my own position, while undogmatic, less equivocal.

M. S. BARTLETT

January 1960

Probability in Logic, Mathematics and Science

1. INTRODUCTORY REMARKS

It is accepted that when words are taken from everyday language and used in a particular field of discourse their meaning should be made as unambiguous and exact as possible. For example, the terms *work, action, energy*, are given precise meanings in physics; and *group, function, imaginary*, in mathematics. This precision is not arrived at immediately, for new concepts and ideas need to settle before they assume definite shape. With these firmer outlines it is, moreover, often possible to distinguish variants from the same source; in particular, the dualism between the mathematical and the physical (for example, between the entity obeying a certain differential equation and the particle causing a track in a Wilson cloud chamber) has long been recognized. To say that the concept of *probability* has not been immune from this dialectic phenomenon is rather an understatement, for the emergence of one or more precise technical meanings for probability has historically been coloured by controversy, which has by no means ended. Confusion still arises from the existence of these different meanings for probability in different fields of discourse, and it is my purpose to survey and if possible to clarify these [1].

In my view the technical meanings and uses of probability can be classified under three broad headings, the difference between variants [2] under any one heading being less fundamental. These three headings relate to the three fields of logic, mathematics and science, and to the corresponding uses of probability in

    (i)   the general theory of inductive inference,
    (ii) the axiomatic mathematical theory of probability,
    (iii) the description and theory of statistical phenomena.

---

[1] Cf. the discussion by E. NAGEL (*Probability and Non-demonstrative Inference*, p. 485) and R. CARNAP (*The Two Concepts of Probability*, p. 513) in *Philosophy and Phenomenological Research*, 5, 1944-1945. *Added in proof:* cf. also the section on probability in BERTRAND RUSSELL's recently published book *Human Knowledge*. London 1948.

[2] No attempt is made here to list all these variants; more detailed accounts will be found in the published literature or in a book by I. J. GOOD shortly to be published: *Principles of Probability and of Weighing Evidence*. London: Griffin.

I have put (i) first because of its all-embracing character, but its very generality is a warning of difficulties, and it will be more convenient to discuss the narrower aspects of probability referred to in (ii) and (iii) before their relation to (i) is examined.

2. The axiomatic mathematical theory of probability

As the theory of probability began from a discussion of the results of games of chance, that is, of particular examples of statistical phenomena, axioms emerging from the historical theory should in particular be appropriate for such applications, and this may be used to formulate them. The simplicity and symmetry of gambling apparatus like dice, roulette wheels or cards led to the idea of equal probabilities or chances, in the sense that the different elementary events were supposed (at first without logical precision) to occur equally frequently 'in the long run'. With the existence of such apparatus in mind, it has often been the practice to arrive at the appropriate axioms by defining mathematical probability, at least to begin with, as a number p associated with the number l of eventualities of a certain type in a class of eventualities of total number m.

At one time I favoured this method of exposition [1], but while the method of arriving at the axioms does not of course affect the mathematical theory if the axioms chosen are the same, or equivalent, it has some bearing on its application, and I now prefer, in setting up the axioms with a view to application to statistics, to adopt a somewhat more direct relation with frequency. Thus if there are k, and only k, mutually exclusive eventualities A_s of the type A, one of which must occur on a 'trial', the associated probabilities p_s are to correspond to empirical frequency ratios r_s/n obtained in n trials. Hence they should be numbers between 0 and 1 satisfying

$$p_1 + p_2 + \ldots p_k = 1 ,$$

and further from the frequency correspondence we require for the probability associated with A_i or A_j a correspondence with $(r_i + r_j)/n$, leading to the additive axiom [2]. The additive axiom also follows from the first approach, if p is defined as l/m, but this is because the use of l/m in contrast with some other function of l/m already implies the additive axiom, as of course it should if we ultimately have the frequency interpretation in mind.

[1] See § II of *The present position of mathematical statistics. J. Roy. Statist. Soc.* 103 (1940), 1.
[2] Cf. the discussion in Chapter 13 ("Statistics and probability") of Cramer's book *Mathematical Methods of Statistics*. Princeton 1946.

On either approach the further multiplicative axiom, which amounts to a definition of conditional probability, follows. That is, if the eventualities A_s are composite ones of the symbolic product type $B_i C_j$, the first approach gives the identity

$$l/m = (t/m)\,(l/t)$$

where t represents the number of eventualities of the type $B_i C$, (i. e. summed over j), and l/t is defined as the conditional probability of $B_i C_j$ with reference to the total class $B_i C$, (i. e. B_i is given). In the second approach, if in addition to the empirical frequency ratio r_{ij}/n, we have the frequency ratio r_i/n for the eventuality $B_i C$, we may write

$$r_{ij}/n = (r_i/n)\,(r_{ij}/r_i)$$

and the corresponding relation between the abstract p-numbers defines the conditional probability of $B_i C_j$ when B_i is given.

The direct frequency approach to the axioms has the further advantage over the first method that the latter makes use of the idea of probability numbers being equal to simple fractions (e. g. $1/2$ for getting ' Heads ' with a tossed coin), and this is strictly a separate idea associated with the symmetry properties of some physical systems.

The above elementary axioms have the limitation that they cannot be applied without extension when the number of eventualities A_s considered is no longer finite; this extension is convenient not only for dealing with variables having a continuous range, but also for demonstrating the relevance of the axioms and the consequent theory when we compare its theoretical predictions with the intuitive ideas about frequency ratios which assisted the setting-up of the axioms.

In this generalization [1], based on the mathematical theory of measure, the additive probability function of the set A_s becomes a completely additive function, such that the probability of any sum of a finite or enumerable sequence of sets is uniquely defined with a meaning consistent with the elementary finite theory.

After the mathematical theory has been set up, its relevance is a matter for general consideration, but in particular its theorems on conceptual frequency ratios in an increasing sequence of independent trials (*independent* being now precisely defined in the theory from the multiplicative axiom) are tests of its appropriateness. We obtain [2] a probability 1 of the conceptual frequency ratio r_s/n tending to the probability p_s, or of r_{ij}/r_i tending to the

[1] See A. KOLMOGOROFF, *Grundbegriffe der Wahrscheinlichkeitsrechnung. Ergebnisse der Mathematik* 2, No. 3. Berlin 1933.

[2] The theorems as here stated belong to the generalized theory, a point once stressed to me in conversation by Prof. Herbert ROBBINS.

conditional probability p_{ij}/p_i (this second result, which is not so often noted, readily follows from r_{ij}/n tending to p_{ij} and $r_i/n \rightarrow p_i$). While the correspondence between a probability 1 and a frequency ratio has become more sophisticated in our generalized mathematical theory, it is natural to allow the correspondence between a probability 1 and certainty in the finitely additive theory to extend to a correspondence with ' almost certainty ' in the completely additive theory. This correspondence entirely fits with the required interpretation; it is not ' certain ', but ' almost certain ' that an ideal coin with probability $1/_2$ of giving heads will give the proportion $1/_2$ of heads in the long run. To make the frequency interpretation self-contained, we finally introduce the postulate that ' almost certainty ', while logically different from certainty, is observationally equivalent.

While attention is being focussed on the axiomatic theory, this last postulate is irrelevant, but it is included here for completeness as part of the discussion on the correspondence of the axioms with the frequency interpretation. The interpretation of probability theory in another more subjective way will be considered presently, but advocates of the subjective interpretation sometimes tend to underestimate the close historical and practical dependence the axiomatic theory in its usual formulation has on the frequency and statistical interpretation.

Two remarks may perhaps be made to support this contention. The positive character of probability numbers, which corresponds to the positive character of observed frequencies, is essential to the proofs of the laws of large numbers. It is to some extent (though admittedly the theory must be handled with more care) possible to generalize the axioms of the mathematical theory to include negative probabilities without affecting the addition and multiplication rules; this generalization has seemed advisable as a basis for negative probabilities which have appeared in recent physical theories [1]. But while such a generalization may sometimes prove mathematically convenient, it is still only the positive probability numbers which can have a direct frequency interpretation and which thus retain a special significance.

The second remark is that the additive axiom for probabilities is an inevitable one if the probabilities are to have a direct correspondence with frequency ratios, but if this correspondence is not made the basis of the axiom but is replaced by a subjective interpretation of probability, the additive axiom becomes much more of a convention [2]. Such a convention

---

[1] See *Negative probability*. Proc. Camb. Phil. Soc. 41 (1944), 71.
[2] See, for example, H. JEFFREYS, *Theory of probability*. Oxford 1939, or E. SCHRÖ-DINGER, *The foundation of the theory of probability*. Proc. Roy. Irish. Acad. 51A (1947), 51 and 141.

may be convenient in order to link with frequency theory or on simplicity grounds, but in my view it stresses the logical distinctness of the frequency theory and the more subjective approach, and also indicates the greater lack of uniqueness in the subjective theory.

3. THE DESCRIPTION AND THEORY OF STATISTICAL PHENOMENA

Since the orthodox mathematical theory of probability has been so closely linked with the frequency or statistical interpretation, it should obviously be appropriate as a mathematical model of actual statistical phenomena, and, incidentally, appears simpler and more rigorous than any alternative statistical theory yet put forward (for example, the one based on von Mises 'infinite Kollectiv'). The practical success of statistical theories in describing observational data in one scientific domain after another is well summarized in Schrödinger's article[1] *The Statistical Law in Nature*, and needs no further justification here. The precise probability meaning of concepts in modern quantum theory I still regard as obscure, but their dependence in some way on probability and statistical ideas is not doubted [2].

What, however, should be made clear is the relation of statistical phenomena and statistical data with the mathematical theory. There is the same dualism here as in science generally between the theoretical concepts and the things perceived. We assume as a hypothesis that the facts are covered by the general theory, and as in other scientific theories we cannot be sure that the hypothesis is true, only learn by experience when the hypothesis appears approximately true to a sufficient extent to be useful. This viewpoint on the scientific status of the concept of statistical probability I have summarized previously [3]. Statistical probabilities envisaged in this way may be termed objective in the sense that while we cannot say they exist exactly in the real world they exist outside ourselves *in the theory*, and can ideally be measured. The criticism has sometimes been made that this ideal measurement does not exactly correspond to anything possible in practice, since it involves an infinite series of trials, but this kind of criticism is not peculiar to statistics. Theoretical methods of measuring other quantitative scientific concepts will be found to be only

---

[1] *Nature* (London), 153 (1944), 704.
[2] Cf H. REICHENBACH, *Philosophic Foundations of Quantum Mechanics*. California 1946; J. E. MOYAL. *Quantum Mechanics as a Statistical Theory. Proc. Camb. Phil. Soc.* (to be published).
[3] *Statistical probability. J. Amer. Stat. Ass.* 31 (1946), 553.

approximately realisable, owing to the inevitable idealisation involved in the theory.

On the above view the status of statistical theory is similar to that of other scientific theories. The question remains: what logical justification have we for making use of it? This question is well-known to be one of the most perplexing in science, and it would be unfair to the statistical theory here summarized to condemn it for not including an answer. It has, however, sometimes been claimed that the answer is provided by the wider subjective theory of probability. I do not agree with this, but I do agree that the meaning, value, and limitations of this subjective theory are worth examination.

4. PROBABILITY IN THE GENERAL THEORY OF INDUCTIVE INFERENCE

In the subjective theory of probability a different correspondence or interpretation of the mathematical theory is set up, and probabilities are interpreted as ' degrees of belief '. It is questionable whether numerical measures of degrees of belief can be assigned to all propositions we may wish to consider, but there seems no doubt that you or I may consider some propositions more likely than others without implying a frequency or statistical interpretation for our assessments. I have mentioned earlier that there is in most approaches of this kind a certain amount of convention, especially in choosing degrees of belief to be between 0 and 1 and on a scale such that they obey the addition axiom for mutually exclusive events. Among these approaches I am inclined to favour most Ramsey's approach [1] by way of expectation. This has the advantage of linking up immediately the probability laws from our present standpoint with those originally discovered in connection with games of chance and stated in § 2, but it does not necessarily restrict probability to its statistical sense unless expectation is similarly restricted. It is of interest that Bayes [2] also defined probability in terms of expectation; there appears to be no very clear evidence, however, to what extent he intended this to be a wider definition than the frequency one.

This association of probability as degree of belief with expectation (e. g. with the amount of money we would wager) determines the scale naturally. For if the occurrence of either of two events means my obtaining

---

[1] F. P. RAMSEY. *The Foundations of mathematics and other logical essays.* London 1931.
[2] T. BAYES. *Phil. Trans,* 53 (1763), 370.

an amount A, my expectation from one event will be greater or less according to my degree of belief being greater or less. If we call B_1 my expectation for the first event, we may write

$$B_1 = P_1 A$$

and take P_1 as the probability. It follows that certainty is denoted by 1, impossibility by 0, and further for the expectation of one or other of two mutually exclusive events, we should have

$$B = B_1 + B_2,$$

whence

$$P = P_1 + P_2.$$

Ramsey showed that the usual rules of probability follow. We have thus reached the conclusion that if you (or I) assign probabilities in this way, they should for logical consistency obey the usual probability rules. We come next to the further point made by Ramsey (*op. cit.*, p. 192); it does not follow that *you*, while agreeing with the rules, will necessarily agree with *my* probability measures, even if you consider your beliefs on the same data. The issue here is fundamental, for Jeffreys in his theory of probability has stated that on a given set of data a probability is unique. The uniqueness of a probability in Jeffreys' theory has to be accepted as an additional axiom, and Jeffreys has noted [1] that without it initial probabilities might logically be assigned in any way. Jeffreys introduces it to link his theory with the general problem of induction, which is then formally solved in terms of these uniquely-determined ' rational degrees of belief '.

My comment on this is that however attractive as a formal solution of the problem of induction, it remains formal because any unique degree of belief postulated in the theory remains undetermined. There is no guarantee that your degree of belief, or mine, will be identical with it; not even any guarantee, as Ramsey observed, that they will agree with each other. We thus have this bifurcation of the theory of probability when treated as a theory of degrees of belief: either we regard it in Jeffreys' sense, in which case the probabilitites in it are undetermined, or else we agree with Ramsey, (cf. also Good, *op. cit.*) to insert in the formulæ our own degrees of belief; in which case the problem of induction reappears, for whose beliefs are to be believed? Essentially the same difficulty has been raised by Eddington in the following remark [2]

[1] *Probability and scientific method. Proc. Roy. Soc.* A 146 (1934), 9.
[2] *New Pathways in Science.* Cambridge 1935, p. 112.

One difficulty in employing strength of belief as a measure of probability is that an expectation or belief has partly a subjective basis. We have agreed that it depends (and ought to depend) on the information or evidence supplied; but in addition the strength of the expectation depends on the personality of the man who weighs the evidence. We try to remove this subjective element by saying that the true probability corresponds to the judgement of a 'right thinking person'; but how shall we define this ideal referee?... Apart from the obvious definition of a right-thinking person as 'someone who thinks as I do' (which is probably the definition at the back of our minds) there seems to be no way of defining his qualities.

Whatever interpretation we place on these degrees of belief, the logical consistency of the theory remains, (that is, consistency among the beliefs of some individual, whether he be hypothetical or actual). In Jeffreys' statement [1] on his theory,

The present theory does not justify induction. I do not consider justification necessary or possible; what the theory does is to provide rules for consistency,

I presume he implies also consistency between individuals, for compare his remark [2]

If the rules of the theory are followed, anybody will get the same answer given the same evidence,

but the possibility or desirability of consistency in this sense is, as we have just seen, not generally accepted. Jeffreys goes some way to achieve it by suggesting rules for evaluating 'prior probabilities' in simplified situations, but the use of these numerical rules in actual problems seems to me misleading through over-simplification. It should be noticed that the simplification involved is different in kind from that used in ordinary scientific (e. g. statistical) theories, for with the latter the weighing of non-numerical factors is still open to us before our final inductive conclusions are made, whereas this is not so if our final induction is supposed to be already contained in the numerical formula. This kind of criticism I do not consider, as Jeffreys has suggested [3], 'to be arguing for indefiniteness as desirable in itself', but as arguing for indefiniteness somewhere in our representation where indefiniteness exists, and for definiteness where definiteness is possible.

I have noted two alternative interpretations of probability as a degree

[1] *Theory of probability*, § 8.8.
[2] See discussion on my paper *The present position of mathematical statistics, loc. cit.*
[3] *Probability and Scientific method, loc. cit.*, p. 16.

of belief. Of these two, I am inclined to be more in sympathy with the one which does explicitly admit that if I am to use the theory I am obliged to insert in the formulæ my own degrees of belief. It is especially in view of the frankly personal character the probabilities then assume in the theory, that I believe it convenient in practice, and indeed an advisable scientific discipline, to keep deductive manipulations of statistical probabilities (which we have seen are logically separate concepts with values theoretically unique and independent of our beliefs about them) distinct.

It is of course true that the theory of degrees of belief can consistently incorporate statistical probabilities in its general symbolism, but they remain a particular class of probability to which it is convenient to give a special name, e. g. *chances* [1]. These chances, since they are in common with other scientific concepts logical fictions, do not correspond with actual degrees of belief, but depend on assumptions which render the corresponding degrees of belief also hypothetical. It is correspondingly important that statisticians should recognize that statistical theory is a deductive theory the relevance of which to the real world rests on induction. This would ensure that the various statistical theorems on estimation, testing hypotheses and confidence intervals are always recognized as part of this deductive theory, with the relevance of these or other theorems to each particular problem still to be considered.

But precisely how such relevance is to be considered must in my view remain, at least partly, with the individual, who will not be unmindful of the *purpose* of his investigation [2]. It is arguable that a correct judgement on the most useful procedure in any situation should itself be an induction based on experience, and certainly my own practice, like that of many other statisticians, has evolved in this way.

M. S. BARTLETT.

---

[1] Cf. *Probability and chance in the theory of statistics. Proc. Roy. Soc.* A 141 (1933), 518.
[2] Cf. the remarks towards the end of his paper by F. J. ANSCOMBE, *The Validity of Comparative Experiments, J. Roy. Statist. Soc.* (to be published).

Some Remarks on
the Theory of Statistics

I. INTRODUCTORY AND HISTORICAL SURVEY.

One of the dangerous trends of modern specialization is that the specialists, especially academic specialists, concentrate either on the theoretical or on the practical aspects of their subject. The physicist becomes dubbed "theoretical" ("mathematical") or "experimental," the economist becomes "theoretical" or "applied" (the division may even be so extreme that only those with the same label will talk to each other). The statistician is not immune from these labels, and the subject I myself officially profess is "mathematical statistics." But I must admit that I am not prepared to defend too strongly the intelligibility of this title, and wonder how it is regarded by this Society, with its traditional emphasis on realism and day-to-day affairs. I would, however, like to talk to you about the *theory* of statistics, for this aspect of statistics I *am* prepared to submit is of complementary importance to the statistics (that is, the statistical data) themselves, and one with which this Society has by its own title some obligation to be concerned.

The point is of course that however much we may wrangle over minor qualificationary conundrums, whether a statistician deserves the name if he does not know the differential and integral calculus (and more of this anon), there is a central theoretical core which unifies statistical disciplines and methods *in whatever field they are used,* and without which any statistical investigation which is more than direct arithmetical counting becomes mere quackery. Notice that in passing I have already indicated what statistics, regarded as a subject, is about. *It is concerned with things we can count.* In so far as things, persons, are unique or ill-defined, statistics are meaningless and statisticians silenced ; in so far as things are similar and definite—so many male workers over 25, so many nuts and bolts made during December—they can be counted and new statistical facts are born. I need not pause long to remind those of you who invariably associate statistics with economics and the affairs of the "State" that this historical association has broadened to the above more general use. The State is still, perhaps even more, concerned with its man-power and production ; but nowadays we are also familiar with, say, the cricket match commentator who concludes his report with some "statistics." [1]

Now we learn to count at school (even if, according to recent findings, rather less accurately than we used to). Why do we need more than arithmetic, and where does statistical *theory* come in ? Clearly arithmetic is one of the first essentials, as Sir Arthur Bowley has frequently stressed, and as all statisticians might do well to remember. *Moreover, our arithmetic is useless unless we are counting the right things,* an

[1] In like vein the *Manchester Guardian* reporter referred to a Test Match innings of the West Indies during their 1950 tour as one "which had seemed to tax to the utmost the analytical researches of statisticians" (24th July), and the *Sunday Times* (23rd July) referred to the records broken in the same innings as giving "the statisticians further cause for satisfaction" !

obvious remark which is nevertheless related to one of the thorniest problems of practical statistics, for example, in the construction or interpretation of statistical tables in economics.

The further step is essentially more advanced and subtle, although it is firmly based on observation of statistics themselves. It is that regularities often appear in our statistical counts when we are dealing with reasonable-sized aggregates, so that the description and behaviour of these aggregates often turns out to be rather simpler and more unified than we might *a priori* have expected. This is indeed fortunate, but statisticians have a thankless enough task in grappling with masses of figures to deserve some such reward. It is on such *observed* regularities that statistical *theory* is based. Perhaps some will shy at this stage, and refuse to worry over such abstract conceptions ; facts, they will say, are good enough for them. But isolated facts have no meaning in themselves, unless they can be incorporated in some pattern or philosophy. As J. M. Keynes once remarked in connection with economic theories ;

> "the ideas of economists and political philosophers, both when they are right and when they are wrong, are more powerful than is commonly understood. Indeed the world is ruled by little else. Practical men, who believe themselves to be quite exempt from any intellectual influences, are usually the slaves of some defunct economist," (*General theory of employment, interest and money*, p. 383).

In the case of statistics, we must not assume that its theoretical side can be assimilated easily, in spite of the optimism of students who expect to absorb it in the course of a few lectures. Statistical facts, in the form of crude censuses, date back to Biblical times ; but statistical theory, and statistical investigations in the modern sense, only date back three hundred years, to the *Natural and Political Observations on the Bills of Mortality* by John Graunt, published in this country in 1662, and to the correspondence in France between Pascal and Fermat on games of chance, written a few years earlier. The fusion of these two sources, the empirical English method and Continental theory, did not really have effect until the last century, when the stream of statistical investigations began to become something of a torrent. Statistical Societies were founded (Manchester in 1833, London in 1834), and Section F of the British Association (Economic Science and Statistical Section, in 1833). The latter, which was honoured at its foundation with the presence of the already famous Belgian statistician, Quetelet, had as its object the promotion of statistical inquiries ; its emphasis was to be on "facts, relating to communities of men, which are capable of being expressed by numbers and which promise when sufficiently multiplied to indicate general laws."

This appears to be a fairly wide definition, but Quetelet's dissatisfaction with it is said to have contributed to the foundation of the London Statistical Society, although their aim, to publish numerical "facts calculated to illustrate the condition and prospects of society" omits to indicate very explicitly any theoretical function related to the existence of those statistical regularities with which Quetelet himself, and Graunt before him, had been struck. (See F. J. Mouatt's, "History of the Statistical Society of London" published in their Jubilee volume, 1885).

While my own object in this paper is to indicate this role of statistical *theory*, there is the difficulty that I do not wish to bore you unduly with its more technical aspects (especially as I have devoted some space to this topic elsewhere).[1] I hope therefore, though with the considerable risk of appearing vague and obscure, that its role will become sufficiently clear from general discussion and examples—examples not only of its use, but of the remarkable line of English statisticians who, while never divorcing theory from practice, have never hesitated to make use of theoretical and mathematical argument where this was needed (*e.g.* Farr, Jevons, Edgeworth, Galton, Karl Pearson, Bowley, Yule, Fisher). Since I might myself be suspected of bias towards the mathematical side, I shall not hesitate to quote where relevant more illustrious and often more economically-qualified authorities. No one, for instance, will probably cavil at Sir Arthur Bowley's early claim (in his

[1] *Journ. Roy. Statist. Soc.* 103 (1940), 1-29.

Presidential address to the Economic Science and Statistics Section of the British Association, York, 1906)[1] :

> " . . . there is no distinction in the nature of things between arithmetical and mathematical statistics ; the distinction to be made is not between the various methods of accumulating and tabulating data, but between the truth and falsity of the reasoning based on the tabulation. Mathematical treatment in the end only furnishes us with a microscope to observe differences which are blurred to the naked eye of arithmetic, and with a method of measurement to aid the judgment too immature to seize the significant fundamental fact concealed by its diverse manifestations. Purely arithmetical work is, however, limited to the tabulation of exact records, where the whole field to be surveyed can be covered, where no approximation or interpolation is necessary, and where statistics becomes only another name for accountancy ; whereas the application of mathematical principles make its possible to measure the inaccessible, to describe the animal from the single bone, to make firm observations from a shifting base, to dispense with the fixed meridian which the base practice of industrial and official needs obscures."

There is, however, one thing I must now go back to, still if possible without becoming too technical. So far my references to the theory of statistics have been vague, but no theory will have much scientific value unless we can fashion it into a precise sharp-edged tool for dissecting and analysing our data. This tool is the mathematical theory of statistical probability. Perhaps if left to English empirical statisticians, who were struggling with rather complicated raw data, this tool would never have evolved so precisely but would have remained a rather blunt-nosed instrument. Fortunately its early development by French mathematicians was based on much simpler statistical phenomena, the counting of heads on the tossing of coins or of sixes on the throw of dice, where the different eventualities could be more easily understood. This enabled a theory to be built up which successfully mimicked the experimental statistical regularities, so that its authors justifiably felt that it gave them further insight into these regularities. Thus de Moivre, who made great contributions to the theory of probability, was led to remark :

[1]See *Journ. Roy. Statist. Soc.* 69 (1906) 540 (541).

"As upon the Supposition of a certain determinate Law according to which any Event is to happen, we demonstrate that the Ratio of Happenings will continually approach to that Law, as the Experiments or Observations are multiplied : so *conversely* if from numberless Observations we find the Ratio of the Events to converge to a determinate quantity . . . , then we conclude that this Ratio expresses the determinate Law according to which the Event is to happen" (*Doctrine of Chances*, 2nd Ed., 1738 ; quoted by H. Westergaard in *Contributions to the history of statistics*, p. 105).

Since these early beginnings, the theory of probability has been applied to more and more complicated statistical data ; it has also invaded and permeated the natural as well as the social sciences. This is because of the essentially statistical nature of so many scientific phenomena, as will be noted again later (§ 3) ; at the moment I merely wish to indicate why the mathematical theory of probability has become so relevant and important. Consider the quotation :

"This science (the theory of probability) has for its main task the study of group phenomena, that is, such phenomena as occur in collections of a large number of objects of essentially the same kind" (p. 1 of A. I. Khintchine's *Mathematical Foundations of Statistical Mechanics*, translated from the Russian by A. Gamow).

Probability theory may thus be said to be the essential mathematical basis of statistical theory ; in fact, there would be little point in distinguishing between them except for a tendency to regard the theory of probability as a branch of pure mathematics, and statistical theory as the application of this mathematical theory to statistical phenomena.[1]

Now it is important to see what this means for statistical method, but I think this will most conveniently be returned to a little later, when I am discussing its (controversial) relevance to economic statistics. First I will conclude this brief historical survey by noting one or two further landmarks where great practical applications followed from theoretical advances. In 1693 the English astronomer Halley published his paper : "An Estimate of the Degrees of the Mortality of

---

[1]There seems no need here to discuss the more controversial aspect of probability theory, connected with the use of the word "probability" in more than one sense ; for my own views on this, see *Dialectica* 3 (1949), 104.

Mankind drawn from curious Tables of the Births and Funerals at the City of Breslaw" (*Phil. Trans.*, 1693), in which the Breslaw statistics were used to construct the first reasonably valid life-table (although Graunt had earlier constructed a more dubious table). Westergaard remarks (*op. cit.*, p. 36) that Halley's contemporaries hardly understood his calculation, and while insurance societies were founded about the same time, it was not till many years later that they adopted Halley's methods of calculating premiums. The debt which actuaries owe to such independent work is enormous, and underlines the suggestion made a year or so ago by Seal that the actuarial profession in this country may be penalizing itself by its tendency to be out of contact with the universities and with modern developments in statistical theory.[1]

Perhaps the great theoretical step among the many advances of the last century was the introduction of the concept of correlation. Chronologically this first appeared in 1846 in a mathematical contribution to the theory of errors by the French astronomer Bravais, but an independent and much wider basis for correlational theory was initiated by Galton in 1888 in his biometric and anthropometric researches ("Co-relations and their Measurement, chiefly from Anthropometric Data," *Proc. Roy. Soc.* 111, p. 135). Karl Pearson has said of this contribution of Galton's :

> "Up to 1889 men of science had thought only in terms of causation, in future they were to admit another working category, that of correlation, and thus open to quantitative analysis wide fields of medical, psychological and sociological research . . . Galton's very modest paper of ten pages from which a revolution in our scientific ideas has spread is in its permanent influence perhaps the most important of his writings." (*Life, Letters and Labours of Francis Galton*, Vol. IIIA, pp. 1 and 56).

[1] I understand, however, that recently revised examination syllabuses for actuaries have given mathematical statistics a more prominent place.

*   *   *

II. RELATION WITH ECONOMIC AND SOCIAL STATISTICS.

The above historical survey will have stressed the close link in the early days of statistical developments between statistics and social problems, especially if, as I think we should, we include the problems arising in vital statistics and in human biology. I have argued that we cannot stop short at arithmetical statistics ; some attempt at understanding the nature of statistical regularities and trends and hence of appreciating the significance of statistical facts is essential. Any argument, however, on the *extent* of the time we spend on theory is likely to be heated, and is reminiscent of the controversy in economics as to how far economic theories are of any use. If they are not, it is high time they were replaced by better ones ; what is nonsense, as I have already suggested, is to argue that no theories (or no facts) are needed, or that the one can do without the other. Can anyone survey the vast edifice of modern science, and not accept the value [1] both of facts and theories, provided that these do not compete but reinforce each other ?

Before the last war there was a curious tendency among some economists to ignore not only statistical theory but also statistical facts (curious after the rapid growth of statistics in the previous century). This certainly contributed to the controversy on the value of economics. The neglect of statistics by the universities in the economic field led the Clapham Committee on the Provision for Social and Economic Research to report in 1946 on the "quite inadequate provision which at present prevails in universities in the United Kingdom for posts in statistics."

In view of this situation, it seems unfortunate that the attempt by the Royal Statistical Society towards the end of the war to set up a Diploma qualification, in order to give statisticians an educational target and to encourage some supply to meet the great demand for statisticians, was attacked by economists (for example, by Austin Robinson in the *Economic Journal* 54 (1944), p. 265). It is true that criticism

[1] I refer here to technical value, and make no moral judgment.

was directed at the syllabus as being too mathematical and out-of-balance : Thus Austin Robinson said (p. 267) :

> "For the economic statistician, mathematical statistics is only *one* of the necessary techniques. It is surely wrong that economic statisticians should be catalogued and classified in relation to one part of their total qualifications, and not in relation to the whole range of them. We should not dream of appraising potential ambassadors *solely* in relation to their linguistic abilities. Similarly we ought not to appraise economic statisticians *solely* in relation to their capacities as mathematical statisticians, but rather in relation to *all* their capacities."

But more than one mathematical statistician, including myself, would have agreed that the syllabus needed revision and in the direction suggested. This hardly justified a purely destructive attack,[1] which, if its argument were accepted, would condemn all paper qualifications and all examinations (including those in economics). Employers look for many things, all important, in employees, for example, the ability to get on well with their colleagues—but the latter requirement does not prevent us trying to train pupils as economists, mathematicians, statisticians or actuaries.

The particular criticism that a good deal of mathematical statistics in the technical sense would never be required by many economic statisticians I would in part support. In any particular job one uses theory or technique only so far as it is necessary ; and certainly, when my job was to deal with production returns for the firm which once employed me, I needed neither. Nor did I need "economics," but I am not going to say that it is in consequence useless. Sir William Elderton pointed out in an open discussion on the proposed Royal Statistical Society Diploma that there is much that we learn at school or university that we do not always explicitly want later, but it may still be invaluable as a training and background. If we are going to consider how much mathematical or theoretical statistics economic statisticians need we have to bear in mind *two* requirements :

[1] I should perhaps stress that I have no wish to resuscitate the particular proposals that led to this controversy, and use this reference as a means of introducing controversial questions which still need to be resolved.

(a) the actual techniques they are likely to want ;

(b) the amount of training in theory and method they
need, to help them acquire a scientific and objective
statistical outlook on economic and social problems.

The second requirement is vaguer but more important than
the first (not only because the techniques are otherwise useless,
but because the good repute of statistics is itself dependent
on it).[1] No adequate recognition and discussion of it, however,
seems to me to be given in Austin Robinson's article.   I am
not going to pretend that mathematical statisticians, anymore
than economic statisticians (if we must have these labels),
know the secret of imparting this outlook, and some of them
have certainly seemed to imply at times the fallacious thesis
that a knowledge of technique is all that matters.   Many
people think that the "flair for statistics" is unteachable, and
is just common-sense—"a kind of luminous common-sense," as
the late Professor Greenwood called it.[2]   Perhaps it is, but
of course, as Voltaire did not hesitate to point out, common-sense
is not so very common.   Speaking of the simplicity of some
of Galton's methods, Karl Pearson (op. cit. p. 50) added :

> "It is the old experience that a rude instrument in the hand
> of a master craftsman will achieve more than the finest tool wielded
> by the uninspired journeyman."

And on the question of how far mathematics was necessary for
statisticians, Greenwood observed (loc. cit.) :

> "In the heroic age of statistics there were John Graunt with
> his shop arithmetic and Edmund Halley, one of the great mathe-
> maticians of his time.   Both made contributions to the science
> which would never be forgotten.   Did anybody doubt who was the
> greater statistician.   Did many doubt that, without Graunt, Halley
> would never have done any statistical work ?"

But, speaking in a statistical sense, I suggest that the advantage
of some mathematical and/or scientific training has been
possessed by the majority of the most eminent statisticians.

[1] Of course the young statistician may by acquiring such an objective
outlook penalize his chances of a successful "career" (see D. Seers'
searing (sic) article in Econ. J. 60 (1950), 622-6).

[2] In the discussion (p. 552) to the paper by J. Wishart on "Some Aspects
of the Teaching of Statistics," Journ. Roy. Statist. Soc. 102 (1939),
532-564.

What seems also clear is that, on the mathematical side, a leaning to the abstract side (while it may assist in contributions to pure theory) may be an actual hindrance to the practising statistician, whose primary function is to "make sense of figures" ; his theoretical knowledge must always be subservient to this end.   We may well recall Keynes' illuminating comment on W. S. Jevons : [1]

> "Jevons was the first theoretical economist to survey his material with the prying eyes and fertile, controlled imagination of the natural scientist.   He would spend hours arranging his charts, plotting them, sifting them, tinting them neatly with delicate pale colours like the slides of the anatomist, and all the time poring over them and brooding over them to discover their secret.   It is remarkable, looking back, how few followers and imitators he had in the black arts of inductive economics in the fifty years after 1862. But to-day he can certainly claim an unnumbered progeny, though the scientific flair which can safely read the shifting sands of economic statistics is no commoner than it was."

To return to my discussion on the Royal Statistical Society's Diploma, I should add that Keynes himself did not favour the first proposals ; but, as far as I am aware, his main objection was that he thought the universities should undertake the responsibility of statistical education.   The more healthy development in university teaching in statistics since the war is thus in line with Keynes' own views, and will, I think, be providing further experimental information before long on what kind of training is *in fact* needed by, and best suited to, various types of statistician.

Let me now return to a point I left in abeyance—how far do statisticians, especially economic statisticians, need to be familiar with the theory of probability ?   If I am right in my suggestion that this is at the root of statistical theory, then *some kind* of familiarity with it is essential.   This seems to be recognized, for example in the following passage [2] by

[1] *Journ. Roy. Statist. Soc.* 99 (1936), 516-555 (524).

[2] See *Journ. Roy. Statist. Soc.* 48 (1885), 595 (616).   I make no apology for such an old reference, for a study of these classical papers often stresses how up-to-date they still are.   For example, some of Sidgwick's comments in this paper on government planning versus private enterprise seem much more sensible than many recent utterances.

Henry Sidgwick (in his Presidential Address on "Economic Science and Statistics" to the British Association, Aberdeen, 1885) :

"Of the method of statistical investigation I have not presumed to speak, as I have not myself done any work of this kind, but have merely availed myself gratefully of the labours of others. But, even so, it has been impossible for me not to learn that to do this work in its entirety, as it ought to be done, requires faculties of a high order. For duly discerning the various sources of error that impede the quantitative ascertainment of social facts, eliminating such error as far as possible, and allowing for it where it cannot be eliminated—still more for duly analysing differences and fluctuations in the social quantities ascertained, and distinguishing causal from accidental variations and correspondences—there is needed not only industry, patience, accuracy, but a perpetually alert and circumspect activity of the reasoning powers ; nor is the statistician completely equipped for his task for discovering empirical laws unless he can effectively use the assistance of an abstract and difficult calculus of probabilities."

Yet in the discussion to the paper of my own to which I have already referred, Bowley, then President of the Royal Statistical Society, appeared to reject my claim for the importance of probability theory. He distinguished three stages in the teaching of statistics—arithmetical, mathematical without probability, application of the concept of probability. He went on to say (p. 22) :

"In my opinion the second stage is more important than the third in relation to economic and kindred problems. Mr. Yule devotes Part II of his *Introduction to the Theory of Statistics* ; Professor R. Frisch's books (*Methods of Measuring Marginal Utility* and *Confluent Analysis*) are wholly or mainly independent of ideas of probability, as is the study by Dr. Tinbergen to which Dr. Bartlett refers. Mr. Yule develops averages, measures of dispersion and the use of frequency curves generally, and the whole apparatus of partial correlation, in his Part II. Mr. Allen and I did not use probability in our *Family Expenditure*. Many other references could be given . . .

Dr. Bartlett's paper . . . limits mathematical statistics . . . to the field in which probability is applied, or, in other words, to the mathematics of sampling. I do not underrate the importance of this field, in which I have worked for many years ; but I do not wish Fellows of the Society to be under the impression that mathematics has no other use, and that before applying it they must master the logical subtleties as well as the analytical difficulties of probability."

My own view, that Bowley is right in one sense and wrong in another, was summed up in my reply (p. 29) ; I was:

"sceptical of the permanence of methods with no theoretical foundation, however much I agree with the President that many statisticians may not need to worry over the 'logical subtleties or 'analytical difficulties of probability theory.' If my motor-car develops engine-trouble, my immediate concern is to find an experienced mechanic, not an expert in thermodynamics."

The significant word in the last sentence is *experienced* ; the mechanic may not be able to pass an examination in thermodynamics, but I would still expect him to attempt only remedies which are in conformity with its principles. Greenwood (*loc. cit.*) has put effectively the same point :

"Sometimes a David felled a Goliath of a statistical difficulty with a smooth stone. It might take a mathematician to prove how truly the stone was aimed."

I suggest that if we really consider the reason why we are so often able to use simple means and dispersion measures (which Sir Arthur Bowley implied are independent of probability theory) or simple frequency curves, we realize that this is merely one manifestation of the statistical regularity of which probability is the theoretical representation. If, for example, "dromedary" (two-humped) distributions were as common as "camel" (one-humped) distributions, simple means and dispersion measures would lose most of their significance. Again, I contend that ideas of statistical stability and sampling are present in almost every *use* made of statistical tables and data, whether or not we explicitly say so. We do not think unreasonable an actuary who uses mortality rates to obtain survival chances and to calculate premiums.

Much has been written about index numbers since Jevons suggested that geometric means have advantages over arithmetic means, but it might be helpful to emphasize more frequently that as weighted averages which claim to be representative of a complex aggregate of quantities they are *all* necessarily limited. Even if a cost-of-living index is based on the mean expenditure of every existing family in the country, its relevance to any particular family at once involves ideas of sampling.

Where we agree is that many practising statisticians, especially in economics, need to have a practical or instinctive, but not necessarily a very technical, appreciation of this. As M. G. Kendall has put it, we all need "the statistical approach" (*Economica* (1950) 127) ; what is not altogether certain, as I have already emphasized in my references to Austin Robinson's article, is how this statistical approach or outlook is best imparted.

I hope with this explanation that any apparent disagreement between Sir Arthur Bowley and myself is at least greatly reduced. Certainly one would not accuse him of ignoring the field of statistical theory and mathematical statistics, either by his work, or by his own pronouncements. I hope he will forgive me if I go back again to his British Association Presidential Address in 1906 (*loc. cit.* p. 545).

"The use of mathematical reasoning in statistics is very imperfectly understood, partly because the passage from numbers to symbols and back to numbers suggests an air of mystery, or even of prestidigitation, to the unmathematical mind ; partly because, even with mathematicians, the application of the theory of probability to the determination of the precision of an estimate is unfamiliar ; partly because the method, though fully sixty years old,* has only recently been developed, and the methods and limitations of its use are still a matter of analysis and discussion among its advocates. In many respects its position resembles that of mathematics in economic theory, a subject handled at length by Professor Edgeworth, my predecessor in this chair in 1889. There are those that hold, in both cases, that verbal or numerical reasoning, unassisted by symbols, is sufficient for the elucidation of all truth. Whatever may be said in favour of this view as regards economic theory—a discussion so familiar to my audience that I need not dwell on it— I do not think that in the case of statistics the argument can be seriously maintained, and it is my intention to give such reasons for this statement as the limitations of a presidential address make possible.

*Quetelet's *Lettres sur la Théorie des Probabilités* was published in 1846."

And further (p. 549) :

> "The region to which I am devoting particular attention is
> that where the theory of probability is invoked, not because there
> are not many other directions in which mathematical methods are
> useful, but because this is of the greatest importance and the least
> generally understood."

*   *   *

III. VALUE AND LIMITATIONS.

I suggested in the preceding paragraphs that the theory of
statistics is needed by statisticians for two reasons (a) as a
definite technique (b) as part of their general background.
Now a little reflection will soon bring home to us some obvious
but important truths about the use of any theory, and in
particular of statistical theory. The *application* of any theory
is necessarily based on approximating assumptions which are
more or less true, and the value of the application will depend
partly on how far the assumptions *are* "more or less true."
These assumptions are technically referred to as the problem
of *specification,* and usually involve the setting-up of some
theoretical frequency distribution or law to be related with
the observed statistical facts, to assist in their interpretation,
and to facilitate further inferences. Some straightforward
distributional examples are (roughly in order of precise validity):
the so-called normal distribution for the velocity components
of gas molecules, the Poisson distribution for the numbers of
emitted particles from a radioactive substance, the binomial
distribution (with 3 : 1 ratio) for the number of tall progeny
in Mendel's genetical experiment on crossing dwarf and tall
peas, the "negative binomial" distribution for the number of
accidents experienced by munition workers, the geometric
distribution for a batsman's number of runs per innings, the
Pareto distribution for the size of incomes. It is no coincidence
that the more exact examples come first from physical and
secondly from biological sources, with social phenomena on
the whole a bad third.

Statistical specifications are now fundamental in the
physical sciences, and the basic reason is not so hard to see.

But inadvertently, as it were, the attitude changes. It dawns upon us that the individual case is entirely devoid of interest, whether detailed information about it is obtainable or not, whether the mathematical problem it sets can be coped with or not. We realise that even if it could be done, we should have to follow up thousands of individual cases and could eventually make no better use of them than compound them into one statistical enunciation. The working of the statistical mechanism itself is what we are really interested in."

In relation to the physical and biological sciences, all this is certainly to me of great interest, but not perhaps of immediate concern to most of you. Now when we come to man, statistical enumerations and hence specifications are apt to be incomplete and insufficient, but again it is clear that they can be of great value for partial descriptions (adequate for particular purposes, such as issuing ration books or assessing life insurance). Moreover, statistical laws *may* tend to operate *in so far* as these statistical descriptions are valid ; they form a partial basis for such phrases as "cumulative causation" and "non-reversible trends" applied to man and his evolving society.[1] There have indeed been recent attempts [2] at propounding mathematical and statistical theories of society (not merely of its economic behaviour), but these appear to me to have suffered from a lack of proportion. It is of limited value to investigate the type of society which results on certain assumptions, unless the investigator undertakes also the responsibility of discussing the extent to which his assumptions are valid (the same criticism applies of course also to the narrower field of economics). But it is perhaps unjustifiable to claim that these investigations, even if they should ideally be a combination of theory and empirical observation, are so far quite valueless. If we study the statistics not of deaths or of heights (which are largely outside our control), but of marriages or of crimes, we find not completely uniform statistical regularity, but superimposed waves correlating with other changing social conditions, so that

[1] Phrases used, for example, by Gunnar Myrdal, of the University of Stockholm, in his Ludwig Mond Lecture at Manchester University on 13th March, 1950.

[2] For example, in N. Rashevsky's book, *The Mathematical Theory of Human Relations*.

THE THEORY OF STATISTICS

Modern atomic theories are concerned with molecules, at
electrons, light quanta, etc., not only existing in large num
but classifiable into groups the individuals of which (at
as far as we can tell) are all exactly alike.   No wonder tha
statistical method is relevant.

Biology is an interesting link between the exact stati
theories of physics and the more doubtful statistical the
of society.   On an individual basis we may study the stru
and behaviour of animals, especially the more complex of t
but no one (I had better say practically no one, and ex
disciples of Lysenko) will doubt the value of studyin
macroscopic behaviour of bacteria, or—if we consider evolt
like Darwin, on a large enough scale, or consider si
aspects of larger creatures, like their genetic structure or
physical measurements—applying statistical theory to
complex creatures also.

The physicist Schrödinger has described this growth
statistical approach in the natural sciences so vividly t
would like to quote, even at some length, his words : [1]

"In the course of the last sixty or eighty years, sta
methods and the calculus of probability have entered one
of science after another. Independently, to all appearanc
acquired more or less rapidly a central position in biology,
chemistry, meteorology, astronomy, let alone such political
as national economy, etc. At first, that may have
incidental : a new theoretical device had become available,
used wherever it could be helpful, just as the microscope, the
current, X-rays or integral equations. But in the case of st
it was more than this kind of coincidence.

On its first appearance the new weapon was mostly accor
by an excuse : it was only to remedy our shortcoming, our ig
of details or our inability to cope with vast observational n
In the study of heredity we might prefer to be able to rec
individual processes of meiosis, and thus to know how the he
treasure of a particular individual is composed from thos
grandparents. In textbooks on gas-theory it has become
phrase, that statistical methods are imposed on us by our ig
of the initial co-ordinates and velocities of the single atoms—
the unsurmountable intricacy of integrating 10^{23} simu
differential equations, even if we knew the initial values.

[1]*Nature* 153 (1944), 704.

society does *partly* act according to a predictable but rather complex statistical pattern. Statisticians of the last century, like Quetelet, were depressed at the suggestion of regularity and law in such statistics, and felt that it was a denial of free-will. But of course external circumstances do condition our decisions, and we are more likely to avoid the fate of ultimate complete regimentation if we can understand soon enough the probable behaviour and evolution of societies "in the large." (I do not mean to imply that such trends are not the result of technical advances in science or of biological factors, or of social catastrophes such as wars, but that we cannot ignore their statistical and cumulative aspects, even perhaps in these so-called causes).

All this, if in a diffuse and general way, is linked with the first broad problem of statistical theory, *specification*. The second broad problem of statistical *inference* has also both its technical and its general aspects. It is concerned with the testing of the specification or statistical model against the statistical data, together with the estimation of averages or other unknown constants, or alternative reduction of the data to workable dimensions. To many, this use of statistical methods for inference purposes represents a fairly well-defined body of technical knowledge, including how to work out means and dispersions, index numbers, regression or correlation coefficients. The wide applicability of some of these methods (which means that they may be of use even when the specification is only vaguely or incompletely known) has led to their playing a special role in the less exact sciences, biology, psychology, and the social sciences, but should not cause us to forget their essential link with, and dependence on, the specification problem.

This point may be illustrated if I remind you of a very ingenious method sometimes available for rendering the specification more definite. In agricultural statistical experimentation where different treatments (or varieties) are to be compared, the plots of ground allocated to the different treatments are chosen according to carefully worked-out statistical principles of experimental design. The same principles operate more generally for any sampling enquiries, and consist of "stratifying" the population to make the sample representative of different sections of the population, but of "randomizing" the choice of the individual units in each stratum, so that each of these units has a statistically equal chance of selection.[1] This particular combination of common and technical sense has given sampling surveys a potential value that has been increasingly recognized. For example :[2]

> "Modern techniques of social research have given statisticians labour-saving ways of finding out all about us. The individual soul that somehow persists inside each 'social unit' may cling stubbornly to the belief that no one can find out everything about the quirks and habits of nearly fifty million people by asking questions of a few 'sample' thousands, but there is an uncomfortable possibility that the sampler can get pretty near the truth."

The United Nations Sub-Commission on Statistical Sampling was recently led to circularize this and other Statistical Societies on the need for more adequate training in the technique of sampling in university curricula.

In certain fields there remain sources of bias, which have been well enough emphasized by the notorious polls on the American election ; with human populations these are mainly due to evasion, either conscious, especially in the case of voluntary enquiries, or perhaps unconscious, especially in the answering of questions with emotional, political or religious content, such as : "Have you any sympathies with the Communist Party ?" or "Do you approve of divorce ?" Even when such biases are present, it is often possible to get further information on them by detailed statistical analysis of the returns.

Having emphasized the link between correct inference and correct specification, I can now turn back once more to the controversial field of economics where the value of statistical theory may still be questioned. This is when we have no precise and carefully planned sampling scheme to analyse but crude observation and fallible statistics. One important class

---

[1] For a recent exposition of sampling techniques, see *Sampling Methods for Censuses and Surveys*, by F. Yates (London, 1949).

[2] *Manchester Guardian* editorial, 1st August, 1950.

of such statistics is that of economic time-series, like unemployment or production. In spite of recent developments in theory (to be referred to again later) enabling us to consider possible specifications or models for such data, we realise at once immense difficulties associated with the complexity and heterogeneity of economic statistical series, contrasted with the brevity of the period usually available for study. In recent years there have been brave and concerted attempts by economists and statisticians (for example, by the Cowles Commission Research Group in the U.S.A.) to analyse such series, adopting the proper logical approach of making as full a specification as possible, based on economic theory, and thus allowing the inference problem some chance by not over-burdening the claims made on it. Those who are interested in this field of statistical activity, and who have not yet done so, should certainly read the exchanges between J. M. Keynes and J. Tinbergen, following Keynes' review of an earlier and perhaps theoretically more dubious statistical approach to these problems by Tinbergen.[1]

The statistician, in this field especially, will do well to remember Keynes' strictures on Tinbergen's work :

> "The worst of him is that he is much more interested in getting on with the job than in spending time in deciding whether the job is worth getting on with. He so clearly prefers the mazes of arithmetic to the mazes of logic, that I must ask him to forgive the criticisms of one whose tastes in statistical theory have been, beginning many years ago, the other way round" (*Review*, p. 559).

But Keynes' final comment was, if still critical, broad-minded enough :

> "No one could be more frank, more painstaking, more free from subjective bias or *parti pris* than Professor Tinbergen. There is no one, therefore, so far as known qualities go, whom it would be safer

---

[1] *Economic J.* 49 (1939), 558 ; 50 (1940), 142 and 154. The publication under review was the first League of Nations volume on the *Statistical Testing of Business Cycle Theories* (Geneva, 1939). In a brief reference of my own (on p. 18 of my previous paper already cited : *Journ. Roy. Statist. Soc.* 103 (1940), 1-29) to Keynes' review, and written before Tinbergen's reply, an indication was given of the probable future development in the logical and technical approach to statistical problems of this type.

to trust with black magic.   That there is anyone I would trust with
it at the present stage or that this brand of statistical alchemy is ripe
to become a branch of science, I am not yet persuaded.   But Newton,
Boyle and Locke all played with alchemy.   So let him continue."

*   *   *

IV. THE TEACHING PROBLEM.

In this paper I have been especially stressing some
controversial points, partly because these affect economic or
practical statisticians as much as anybody, and partly because
this is a good opportunity anyway to air these problems.
As a teacher of statistics I am necessarily concerned with the
teaching problem ; but if I now consider this problem for a
moment I hope, in spite of my own rather fleeting references
to the part of statistical technique and theory which is of
acknowledged and fundamental value, that this fact will be
generally acceptable, so that I may concentrate on the questions
of *how much* of this various students need, and how they can
best acquire it.

My own teaching experience is somewhat limited, but as
far as it goes it suggests to me (as is doubtless felt by most
other teachers !) that achievement has been very partial and
variable.   Some mathematicians are inclined to lap up the
mathematical theory but to remain half-morons about its
statistical and arithmetical applications ; research workers in
other subjects may learn the techniques diligently but remain
crippled over their theoretical meaning and intelligent use.
Fortunately there are always at least a few in either camp
who do better than the rest ; these are the ones who think
out what they are doing, and never apply methods merely
as a routine.   But to teach all students to *think* ; who would
not like to have the secret of that ?

The departmentalism of a university is also a dangerous
canalising influence.   It inclines one to teach statistics to
mathematicians as mathematics, and so accentuate their
tendency to abstraction, too much of which we have seen is
not a good training for statisticians ; and it inclines one to

avoid teaching theory to non-mathematicians, because they don't know enough mathematics. Departmentalism has especially been bad for statistics, because of the way this subject straddles more than one department ; university departments are on the whole organised on the "vertical" principle, and not the "horizontal" one, and subjects which do not dovetail entirely within one department are liable to be chopped down until they do. The perplexed departmental statistician then has the dilemma of narrowing his statistical interests to those of his own department, but with little machinery for contact with relevant statistical work outside it ; or of attempting himself the superhuman task of keeping abreast with all developments, with perhaps little thanks for his pains. This dilemma is not peculiar to universities. It has appeared, in one guise or other, in research institutes and the Civil Service ; for the latter, the Government innovation of a Central Statistical Office, which is linked with, but not a substitute for, the several departments, is a possible help.

To return to the students, I shan't say much more about the mathematicians. Given time enough, the statistically- and practically-minded of them can get training in methods and some acquaintance with statistical research work, especially since the introduction into some universities, partly inspired by the Royal Statistical Society's proposals, of a post-graduate Diploma in Statistics. Their absorption of statistical ideas is undoubtedly slow, but this is partly due to the complete absence of statistics in school curricula, and may be altered if recent proposals to introduce statistics into schools are generally accepted. Whether or not these proposals are a good thing is another controversial story, and is probably dependent on the departmentalism difficulty. As *mathematics* we have seen that statistical theory is necessarily rather abstract, because it deals not with things themselves, but with aggregates of things. But the actual *statistics*, as numbers of births and deaths, measurements of heights and weights, bowling and batting averages, numbers of cars passing in the street, seem very real and (rather unexpectedly) dear to the hearts of many school children. Later more serious study might well be founded on such a basis.

The next problem is who should teach statistical theory and methods to the non-mathematicians—the biologists, the psychologists, the economists, the medical students? Should it be a mathematician, who will perhaps be too abstract for them and not appreciate their practical problems, or someone from their own department, maybe a little shaky himself on the mathematical and theoretical side?[1] I personally think that there is no cut-and-dried answer to this query; successful teaching is largely a prerogative of the individual, and a capable teacher may be better than a better expert in either capacity. Criticism in the past has largely been levelled at the habit, in either the mathematics or in the other departments, of asking people to teach statistics who were not even statisticians. There has been some excuse for this in poorly-staffed departments, but this dangerous custom should disappear as statisticians become more recognized as persons in their own right and less rare.

Finally, we come to the problem of what to teach; though this is not such a problem in most departments. For example, the methods used in biological statistics are pretty well-defined, and I have discussed elsewhere[2] draft syllabuses for them. I have already stressed the danger of too narrow a training and neglecting proper grounding in statistical principles, but for the more mathematically-minded at least it should be possible to avoid this danger. Even for the others, provided they become statistically-minded, provided they learn principles by enough practice, perhaps by examples not all from their own subject, sufficient grounding may be acquired. Many biologists have shown considerable aptitude in this. Principles in relation to medical statistics are perhaps a little less definite (excluding particular technical fields such as vital statistics or epidemiology), and in saying this I am not being inconsistent with my earlier claim that principles remain common and

[1]Compare the discussion by C. Herdan in the *Universities Review* 23 (1950), 30-6.
[2]*Biometrics* 6 (1950), 85.

inviolate, because now I am discussing rather how such principles are best illustrated in particular fields. And again the problem becomes perhaps most acute of all in economics, for reasons already considered at length. Not only must considerable attention be paid to the details of definition, collection, and comparison of statistics (this holds also, though perhaps not to such a variety of data, for medical statistics), but we have no clear-cut applications of principle yielding immediate and obvious returns, as in the case of the natural sciences. The relation between principle and practice is more elusive and tenuous.

I am not going to presume to say how this difficulty is to be met : I have suggested that further teaching experience will provide us before long with more evidence, and I hope economists in the audience will add their opinions to the pool (whirlpool?). What I *have* maintained is that statistical principles must not be neglected, and a fairly common practice at present of having a mixture of mathematicians, biologists, and economists taking a basic course in statistical principles, while it may have arisen from teaching economies, may perhaps be useful (provided the course does not get too mathematical) for the economists in particular, because they may have a better opportunity of grasping these principles in examples from other fields, and thus of realising more clearly the special features of their own subject which render the application of these principles more nebulous. But some mathematical ability is undoubtedly a great help, and the comment [1] of C. F. Carter, who teaches economic statistics at Cambridge, is worth noting :

> "There was one further point which appeared to him to be rather serious. It seemed to him that the educational system in our schools produced either people who were good at mathematics, . . . or else people who had a fear and loathing of mathematics. There were not [2] very many people in between those two classes.

[1] p. 220 of the discussion on the teaching of statistics, *Journ. Roy. Statist. Soc.* 111 (1948), 212-229.

[2] I have checked with Mr. Carter that this word "not" was inadvertently omitted by the printer.

There were few who were ready to say that they were moderately good at school at mathematics and were quite ready to go on learning. If they could be sure of having people coming to the university or to an extra-mural course with a basic knowledge of mathematics, their task would be immeasurably easier."

* * *

V. MODERN DEVELOPMENTS.

To conclude, I would like to review briefly and non-technically some modern theoretical developments. If I were asked to name the main developments in statistical *theory* in the present century, I should certainly include the tremendous growth in the use of statistical methods and statistical inference in biology and other sciences, begun by Francis Galton, and Karl Pearson, and culminating in the work of R. A. Fisher. Often this development has resulted in simpler but more powerful methods, such as the partial ousting of correlation technique by the method known as "analysis of variance," which is a basic technique for exploring complex sources of variation and analysing them into their various components. First used in agricultural experiments, its general applicability later resulted in its use in industrial research, and in many other fields of statistical experimentation. It has greatly influenced the efficient design of experiments, and of sampling enquiries, being of greatest value and simplicity for experimental or other statistically-controlled situations.

I shall not discuss any further the advances in statistical specification in the natural sciences, for example, in physics or in biology, for I have already sufficiently indicated the revolutionary advances which a statistical outlook has brought about. What I will do is to indicate two major and related tasks which are confronting the theorist who has an interest in applications, and which have emerged more clearly since I last surveyed the field of mathematical statistics over ten years ago (*loc. cit.*). The first will not sound unfamiliar to economic theorists, who have been attempting in recent years to move from "static" to "dynamic" conceptions of how things work, for this is a fundamental statistical problem also, with far-reaching applications in all branches of science. The economic and statistical problems are naturally related in the field of economics itself, and a good deal of recent work on the analysis of economic time-series has been based on this new approach. But of course it applies also to changing populations, to the rise and fall of epidemics, to the showers of particles created by cosmic rays, to the periodicity of the sunspots, and so on. A recent example in the field of electrical engineering has been the development of a basic theory of communication systems (with. repercussions even on the understanding of man's personal communication or *nervous* system).[1] `

These various examples have stimulated a study of the general mathematical theory of this kind of statistics ; this has now been in process of development for some years, being first studied systematically on the Continent as an extension of the theory of probability ; but a tremendous amount needs to be done to integrate this theory with particular applications, especially where problems of statistical inference arise. Already, however, a much completer understanding of the structure and analysis of time-series has emerged, though I should perhaps add a warning that the more the understanding of the problem the greater the realisation of its complexity.

The gap between theory and practice is always in part due to an over-simplification or idealisation of the actual situation, and just as it is often more relevant to consider, not the static homogeneous population or distribution of classical statistics, but populations which grow and distributions which change, so also it may be more relevant to consider complex populations and heterogeneous distributions. This has of course been recognized in the direct handling and analysis of real populations, for example, in the "break-down" of statistical

A technical account of this theory of stochastic processes, as it is called, with discussion of its applications to theories of population growth, physical processes, epidemiology, industrial renewal theory, etc., will be found in the papers by D. G. Kendall, J. E. Moyal and myself, given at a Symposium on Stochastic Processes, and published in the *Journ. Roy. Statist. Soc. (Series B)* 11 (1949), 150-282. For a monograph on economic aspects, see *Statistical inference in dynamic economic models* (New York). For the theory of communication, see C. Shannon's papers in *Bell System Tech. J.* 27 (1948), 379 and 623.

totals, in sampling techniques, or in analysis of variance, but the *theoretical* behaviour and analysis of complex groups has been less systematically studied, in spite of important pioneering investigations such as Greenwood and Yule's (1920) discovery of the negative binomial distribution as the result of heterogeneity in accident-proneness among different workers.[1]

I said that these two studies, of changing populations and of heterogeneous populations, were related. For example, if a population is growing then the existing population at any time is necessarily a complex and heterogeneous one. Moreover, it has been found that observed distributions can arise in various ways ; the negative binomial distribution, for example, not only arises from heterogeneity between groups, but from "contagion" in time, say if each worker who had an accident became more nervous and more inclined to have a second. In fact the negative binomial distribution was first deduced on such a "contagion" model by McKendrick in 1914, working in medical statistics. Thus we realise that the total distribution itself will not discriminate between these two possibilities, and a more detailed study of changes in time will be required to eliminate the second.

Finally, this more complex but more realistic conception of a statistical population, changing and heterogeneous;[2] appears to me to underline further the central place of sampling notions in statistical theory. We cannot any longer claim that actual populations are large enough to forget about such ideas ; we must find out how non-uniform such populations are, and the effectively uniform groups—the local number of susceptible persons in contact with an infected person ; or the number of workers of one district, one age, one occupation, and one disease—may invariably be small enough to make sampling questions permanently relevant to any theoretical and inductive conclusions we may make.

---

[1] Another important though rather technical problem which has of course already received considerable attention is that of the genetical structure of populations (see, for example, Sewall Wright's Galton Lecture, 14th June, 1950, printed in *Nature* 166 (1950), 247).

[2] Professor Leontief recently remarked to me that he believed it important to take account of the "heterogeneity" as well as the overall time-changes when analysing economic series.

Factor Analysis in Psychology as a Statistician sees it

1. The historical and the logical approach

Historically, from its introduction, factor analysis has been a matter of some considerable argument and controversy. Some psychologists may perhaps have been sufficiently put off by exaggerated claims from their colleagues as to query its use at all in their field. The growth of factor analysis must, however, be regarded as a natural and inevitable development in the analysis of the correlated sets of test scores or other variables with which psychologists have had to deal. But even psychologists and statisticians interested in the technique of factor analysis have been somewhat bewildered by the variety of procedures advocated from time to time in the literature; and while the energy and occasional acrimony of the discussion has been an indication of the interest the subject has possessed in the eyes of its protagonists, it has tended to make those not yet involved pause before themselves being drawn into the mêlée. It is probably a matter of statistical fact that any argument usually arises when each side is partly right and partly wrong. In the case of factor analysis we have by now reached a stage in its development when we can attempt to survey this subject not only historically but also logically; this may help us to appraise its validity and use. This does not, however, imply that such a survey was possible at the very beginning, before techniques had been explored or experimental material collected. We shall also realise the limitations of a purely logical approach, and the extent to which there is legitimate scope for further discussion and investigation. It is hardly necessary for me to add that there are now several authoritative books and articles on factor analysis in psychology (see, for example, 7, 8, 12, 14, 15 and 16 in the list of references), the existence of which makes superfluous not only any detailed description of some of the more accepted techniques, but also much of my present commentary. However, an indication of one's personal view may still be useful, especially in relation to those aspects on which the last word has clearly not yet been said.

Suppose a statistician were confronted with a set of examination scores (or scores from 'intelligence tests' in the more specific sense) for a number of children. He would be aware from his general statistical philosophy that he would have two broad tasks facing him, the first of specification, in which some kind of theoretical statistical model for the observed data has to be set up, and the second of inference, in which the data are analysed according to, and checked against, this model. In many routine statistical problems, especially those of an empirical kind, the first task is sometimes forgotten, but it is essential before the second can begin. *Qua* statistician, he may feel that it is not *his* responsibility, and it is certainly not *merely* his; but he must be able to collaborate, or at least to concur, with (in this case) a psychologist in arriving at a suitable specification, relevant and reasonable from both the psychologist's point of view and his own. The statistician's participation in the specification (this follows automatically of course if he and the psychologist are the same person!) is essential because it must include and depend on the purpose of the analysis, a point which has not always been appreciated. The same data may well be specified differently for different purposes, and there is nothing inconsistent in two specifications, one of which is very general and corresponds to an empirical type of analysis, and another equivalent to a detailed statement of structure which the analysis has merely to verify or refute. Technical difficulties in a statistical analysis may lead to approximating simplifications over the validity of which there is temporary discussion, but it is obviously in the specifications, which can include all categories from minor assumptions to full-blooded scientific theories, that there is room for legitimate argument. If we find more than one statistical procedure being advocated, for example in factor analysis, one immediate task is to enquire into their respective purposes: only if these are close do we need to compare the associated models further.

2. The empirical statistical approach

When statistical material arises in a complex and comparatively unexplored field it is often reasonable to leave its specification as general as possible, at least until further experience about the character of its variability has been obtained. It is in such situations that careful experimentation, coupled with the use of analysis of variance technique, can throw a flood of light on the relative importance of different sources of variation. A well-known example is in agriculture, but psychology offered in many respects a similar opportunity; for example, the effects of sex, age and social group all needed disentangling in children's test performances.

However, the statistical tool made available to psychologists by Galton before the beginning of the present century was correlation, so it is not perhaps surprising that the use of this technique has at times appeared almost excessive. Nevertheless, the occasions when a number of scores in tests or other 'measurements' was available for a group of persons under investigation, with the question naturally arising of their mutual relation, were frequent enough. An empirical reduction of such data by the method of principal components could have been used, for, as Sir Cyril Burt (8) has pointed out, this method had already effectively been put forward by Karl Pearson in 1901.

For reference this method is summarized briefly here. Suppose we have a set of p correlated test scores or other variables, represented by the (column) vector x, measured from their mean values, and for definiteness standardized to unit standard deviations, so that their correlation matrix is given by

$$R = E\,(x\,x'),\qquad(1)$$

where E denotes averaging over the statistical population (and a dash denotes a transposed matrix or row vector). Then the solution α_i of the simultaneous linear equations

$$(R - \lambda_i)\,\alpha_i = 0\qquad(2)$$

gives a principal component $z_i = \alpha_i' x$ corresponding to the root λ_i of the determinantal equation

$$|R - \lambda| = 0.\qquad(3)$$

The z_i, which are also for convenience usually standardized, have the property that they are not only uncorrelated, but the vectors α_i for different i are orthogonal (i.e. $\alpha_i'\,\alpha_j = 0$). A more essential property from the point of view of the reduction or summary of the data is that they extract successively the maximum contributions to the sum p of the (standardized) variances, these contributions being given by the values of the roots λ_i themselves when arranged in order of magnitude. The machinery for their computation if the correlation matrix R has merely been estimated (as R_0, say) from a sample of persons is similar. The z_i are in one sense 'factors', but more in relation to the diagonal variance contribution than in the reproduction of the correlations, a rather significant point.

Such an empirical analysis is helpful in the description of the data, but does not (no more of course would any other 'factor analyses' carried out without reference to external criteria) have any necessary significance outside it. The statistician is aware of entirely different methods of multivariate analysis introduced by Hotelling for studying the relation of one set of variables to another. Typical applications of this in psychology would be to study the possible relations between physical and mental measurements, or to study the relation of a set of mental measurements at one time with another set taken on the same persons at a future time (cf. 4). A particular case of this last problem is the prediction of future performance in some one test or other classifiable criterion, this, as Sir Godfrey Thomson has stressed, reducing to an application of standard multiple regression technique.

3. Theories of factorial structure

It seems probable that the more theoretical factor analysis schemes preferred by many psychologists have largely developed as a historical consequence of the original formulation of this type by Spearman, who initially postulated the simple factor model of one general factor g and uncorrelated remaining components s_i specific to each test x_i, so that we have

$$x_i = m_i g + \sqrt{1 - m_i^2}\, s_i, \tag{4}$$

where g and s_i, like x_i, are assumed standardized.

There is no doubt that such a model was a vivid and useful first approximation to the truth, but when it became clear that it was inadequate, and further 'common factors' had to be introduced, the arguments intensified over the question of the 'reality' of the factors in the consequent more general specification

$$x_i = m_{i1} f_1 + m_{i2} f_2 + \cdots m_{ik} f_k + m_{i0} s_i. \tag{5}$$

In vector and matrix notation, this last set of equations becomes

$$x = M f + M_0 s, \tag{6}$$

say, where $f' \equiv (f_1, f_2, \ldots, f_k)$ and M_0, from (5), is a diagonal matrix.

One source of difficulty has been the apparent redundancy of factors in (5) (and, for that matter, in (4)), if the residual components s_i are interpreted, as in (4), as factors specific to each test; some further explanation is thus needed. But I see no objection to the view that the correlational structure is to be interpreted by means of as few *common* factors as possible. It is now appreciated that the isolation and measurement of a few such factors, especially if a large amount of variability remains in the specifics, is not of much direct prognostic value. As Godfrey Thomson has said (15):— "Very seldom have experimenters actually calculated the factors possessed by a man and used them to give him advice." The main object of the analysis, in so far as it has been specified at all, is presumably to assist in the understanding and interpretation of the test performances. Now something more has been envisaged here than a mere description or summary of the data, even although there is no *guarantee* that any factors isolated have any significance outside it, and we must be on our guard against assigning prematurely any degree of 'reality' to them beyond their definition in the statistical specification (6).

With this point of view the search for factors with a more permanent and universal character is scientifically reasonable, but seems to me likely to be more successful if the specific 'factors' in (6) are retained. It is inevitable that in so far as (6) is true at all, it is an over-simplification which explicitly ignores such possibilities as variation in performance at different times or variation in the matrix of coefficients M from person to person, and thus the specific 'factors' s_i are composite items which must implicitly include all these sources of variability. If so, it seems logical to retain them in the model, and regard them, in regard to the measurement of the more stable and common features of the test scores, as 'errors' (though this does not imply that they are merely 'errors of measurement', a rather important distinction to which I refer again later). In the paper from which I quoted a moment ago, Godfrey Thomson goes on to raise the question whether it would not be more useful to exclude the specific factors from equation (6) (cf. also the discussion in the last chapter of his book (14)). This, as I have emphasized, depends on our purpose, but as for the above reasons we should not expect to be able to exclude them entirely I think it would be rather illogical to try to do so in any search for stable factors, a search which is circumscribed in its use but will nevertheless no doubt continue.

4. Estimation procedures and tests of goodness of fit

The estimation and testing of a factorial structure should strictly precede any consideration of the estimation of the factors for a particular person, though historically, at least in so far as any rigorous statistical discussion is concerned, the reverse appears to have been the case. This may in part have been due to the difficulty of the complete estimation and testing problem, in which some questions still remain unsolved. However, we now have one method at least, the 'method of maximum likelihood' applied by D. N. Lawley (11) to the sample covariance or correlation matrix R_0 corresponding to the theoretical

$$R = M M' + M_0^2, \tag{7}$$

4

which should in principle, as far as we know at present, give a satisfactory solution of the problem of estimating structure when the test scores are normally distributed (and if the number of tests is adequate to permit a solution at all). Lawley's estimation equations for M and M_0 may be summarized as

$$M' R_0^{-1} R = M', \tag{8}$$

together with the requirement that the diagonal elements in R and R_0 agree. It is an attractive feature of these equations that they are effectively independent of whether R is the matrix of covariances or correlations. Unfortunately no very rapid method of solving the equations is as yet available, so that illustrations of their actual use in psychology are rather rare (as one interesting example, see, however, an analysis by Emmett (9)). Lawley has also shown that a large-sample χ^2 goodness of fit test of the adequacy of the assumed structure in (7) can be made, and I have noted (5) that a somewhat more precise formulation of this test would be expected to be

$$\chi^2 \sim -\{n - \tfrac{1}{6}(2p+5) - \tfrac{2}{3}k\} \log_e |R_0| / |R|, \tag{9}$$

with $\tfrac{1}{2}(p-k)(p-k-1) - k$ degrees of freedom (in this formula n is the number of degrees of freedom in R_0 depending on the number of individuals tested, p the number of tests, and k the number of common factors; $|R|$ denotes the determinant of R, and similarly for $|R_0|$).

This approximate χ^2 technique may also be used with the alternative principal components analysis referred to earlier, the criterion taking the same form as in (9) with $|R|$ replaced by

$$\lambda_1 \lambda_2 \dots \lambda_k \left(\frac{p - \lambda_1 - \lambda_2 \cdots - \lambda_k}{p - k}\right)^{p-k}, \tag{10}$$

where the λ_i in (10) are the latent roots of R_0 (see 5, 6). The effective number of degrees of freedom for χ^2, in the usual case where R refers to the correlation matrix, depends on how large the eliminated principal components are, but it is safest for $k \neq 0$ to allocate the degrees of freedom $\tfrac{1}{2}(p-k-1) \cdot (p-k+2)$. The purpose of the χ^2 test here is to test the homogeneity of the correlation structure after the first k principal components have been removed, but it should be realised that as no specific factors are being retained it is quite possible for all p principal components to be found significantly separable.

If it is assumed that the factorial structure has been obtained from a large enough group to be well-determined, the actual values for these factors in the case of a particular individual, who may or may not have been in the originally tested group, may then require estimation. My own view here is in accordance with the idea of searching for a few common factors, in the determination of which the remaining variability, whether or not attributable to genuine specific factors, is necessarily 'error' in the broad sense. It was this approach which led me (2) to put forward the common factor estimates for any person

$$f_e = J^{-1} M' M_0^{-2} x, \tag{11}$$

which for random variation of this so-called 'error' are unbiased with variance-covariance matrix[1]

$$J^{-1} \equiv (M' M_0^{-2} M)^{-1}. \tag{12}$$

It is of course true that the hypothetical factor-structure embodies the specification that the factors are standardized over all persons, and Godfrey Thomson has used this property to deduce an alternative set of estimates f_t, say. These he has called 'regression' estimates, and they have the property that while biassed for any particular person towards the zero values representative of the average person, their mean square deviations from the true values are a minimum when considered for all persons. Any argument as to which estimates are preferable in any situation could hardly proceed further without some specification of their purpose, and in any case hardly arises in connection with statistical investigations over the whole group of persons, as the two sets of estimates are equivalent as a reduction of the data. They are obtainable one from the other by the relation

$$f_t = K f_e, \tag{13}$$

where $K = M' R^{-1} M$. The estimates f_t have the property that, when averaged over all persons,

$$E\{(f_t - f)(f_t - f)'\} = I - K. \tag{14}$$

An alternative to the two-stage procedure of factorial structure estimation and factor estimation is to attempt to resolve the over-all estimation problem at a single stage directly from the observations. This at first sight appears attractive, but unfortunately it has been found impossible without some further assumption. In a recent re-examination of this approach, Dr. Whittle (17) has suggested making some further assumption on the relative magnitude of the 'residual error' variances. It is not entirely clear to me whether he intended by this phraseology to include specific factor variances

---

[1] There *is*, in spite of an implication to the contrary by M. G. Kendall (12 § 31), a definite sampling interpretation possible of this error (see 3).

in his 'residual error', but if so I am inclined to think that the possibility of having such further precise information becomes more doubtful. An apparent advantage of this approach is the resulting symmetry between persons and tests, but although it is admittedly important to consider the tests as a kind of sample of possible tests available for measuring a person's common factors (partly analogous to our sample of persons), I do not consider the relation so completely symmetrical as has sometimes been implied.[1] Nevertheless, there is no doubt that a further assumption about the 'residuals' does considerably simplify the problem, and further clarification and discussion of it would be useful. (Dr. Lawley has pointed out to me in correspondence that while such an assumption does not appear *essential* in his alternative approach via the covariance matrix, it renders more practicable not only the estimation of M but the assessment of its accuracy.)

5. Interpretation of factors

The common factors in the estimation equations (8) (as in any alternative estimation equations) are, even if specified to be uncorrelated, not unique, for appropriate linear combinations ('rotations') of the common factors may equivalently be chosen. While they may be made unique by a canonical definition within the set of common factor rotations, analogously to the definition of principal components, this is of course an empirical step, and *if* some kind of stable factors can be envisaged beyond the framework of the particular tests employed, then there is no reason why the canonical set corresponding to a particular set of tests should coincide with them without further rotation.

There seems no objection therefore to a search for the most economical, simple or stable set of factors within the admissible framework, and here the custom of American psychologists, and in particular L. L. Thurstone (16), appears to have developed somewhat differently from the British school. I shall not attempt to examine any such divergences, especially as I cannot claim to be familiar with the American work; it is moreover not merely a statistical matter. But it should be emphasized that only in so far as a particular choice leads to further simplification or confirmation beyond the particular data analysed has it any superior merit to statistically equivalent choices, selection among which is otherwise arbitrary.

For similar reasons, while it is perhaps a useful and stimulating incentive

---

[1] To be so the 'tests' must, like the persons, constitute a reasonably homogeneous statistical population; in my opinion this implies a rather narrow conception of different tests (cf. 1).

to investigation to have some more ultimate interpretation or identification of factors in mind, no valid scientific discrimination between rival interpretations is possible for which the observational consequences are the same. It seems to me to have been a most salutary warning to the protagonists of the idea that factors are real and indecomposable entities when Godfrey Thomson (see, for example, 14) put forward his 'sampling interpretation' of factors, in which he suggested that one might regard the mind as a synthesis of a large number of components or 'bonds', of which only a portion or 'sample' will be manifested in any particular test.

The striking feature of this interpretation was the emergence of statistical entities with all the properties of general, group and specific factors from a structureless population of elements. Thus I have shown (1) how, if this sampling theory were assumed, a rigorous definition of all such factors could be given in terms of it. For simplicity rather than necessity, we can consider a model in which all the basic components are independent and of equal 'weight'. Then for any individual the mean value of all his components (or at least all those which may be sampled by tests of some class under consideration) is defined as his 'general ability' g. A specific factor s is merely the contrast between the mean value of the components sampled by a particular test, and the average g of all components. If two tests each represent random samples from all the components, the specific factors s_1 and s_2 corresponding to the two tests will be independent. If they are not random samples, but are taken from a subset of the entire set of components, they will be correlated, and it will be necessary to introduce a further 'group factor' to account for this correlation. Arbitrary rotation of the general and group factors so defined to any equivalent set of common factors is of course possible as before.

I argued further at the time that such a statistical interpretation of factors would not rule out their possible usefulness, provided we realised their essentially statistical definition and consequent limitations. Their essentially statistical character is in fact not dependent on the above interpretation, for they can in any case only be defined in relation to some statistical population of persons. If we change this population by selection, the factors will change too (see 14 Pt. V), but this does not necessarily invalidate their study. For example, if we consider the above model of countless independent components, we should expect a development of correlations among such components from genetic causes, due to the existence of homogamy for mental as well as physical traits, and leading to some enhancement of general and group factors at the expense of specific factors (2).

6. The hypothesis of linearity

A few moments ago I suggested that while interpretations of factors extending beyond the statistical consequences so far confirmed are not in any scientific sense established, they may be a useful stimulant to further research. Sooner or later it will be necessary to consider mental activity in terms of the functioning of the brain, and Godfrey Thomson's interpretation may be regarded as a first attempt in this direction. Burt, however, has argued with some justification that an intelligent mind is likely to be characterised by the brain's capacity for systematization and organisation, and thus adds (7 p. 217): "I lay more stress on the *systematization* of 'bonds' . . . than upon the mere *number* of bonds." This emphasis on nervous organisation and pattern has recently been developed at considerable length by Hayek (10). Now such a modified and probably more realistic conception of the brain's mode of behaviour does not in itself invalidate Thomson's Sampling Theory as a *statistical model*; this appears to me to remain an *admissible* interpretation at least as long as we adhere to the factor model (6). If anyone wishes to reject Thomson's theory as an inadequate model, I maintain that he must first ask on what evidence he could reject the assumptions of addivitity and linearity on which the model (6) is based. Such assumptions would seem unlikely to be true on the basis of the above more complex ideas about mental activity except perhaps as a first approximation. It is here where there is a complete contrast between the empirical principal components analysis and the hypothetical factor model (6). The former is by definition linear and additive, and no question of a hypothesis arises. The latter, on the other hand, includes what for definiteness I shall term the hypothesis of linearity, which, although it might be expected to work as a first approximation even if it were untrue (cf. the example discussed by Godfrey Thomson in Ch. 12 of his book (14)), would in principle have to be rejected in favour of a more complicated model if the evidence demanded it.

It is important to notice that as correlation is essentially concerned with linear relationships, it is not capable of dealing with this point. As, for the reasons indicated, I think it has some scientific interest, I propose to discuss it a little further in this concluding section of my paper. The basic formulae will be evident enough if I illustrate them in the hypothetical case of two common factors f_1 and f_2. In this case, if we suppose that the linear model

$$x_i = m_{i1} f_1 + m_{i2} f_2 + m_{i0} s_i \tag{15}$$

is insufficient, it would be expected mathematically that as the next approximation we should have the relation

$$x_i = m_{i1} f_1 + m_{i2} f_2 + m_{i3} f_1 f_2 + m_{i4} (f_1^2 - 1) + m_{i5} (f_2^2 - 1) + m'_{i0} s'_i \qquad (16)$$

where it is assumed that f_1 and f_2 are uncorrelated and in standardised measure (i.e. zero means and unit standard deviations over the population of persons tested). If equation (16) held, and we supposed for definiteness that f_1 and f_2 were normally distributed, then the further quantities

$$f_3 \equiv f_1 f_2, \quad f_4 \equiv (f_1^2 - 1)/\sqrt{2}, \quad f_5 \equiv (f_2^2 - 1)/\sqrt{2}, \qquad (17)$$

while not normal, could otherwise act just like further common factors *as far as the correlation properties of the test scores are concerned.* It is true that x_i in (16) would also not be exactly normal, but if it is remembered that the original x_i distribution may deliberately be transformed to normality, this would not seem to have any great significance. It might also be objected that as the factors f_1 and f_2 are themselves derived in the first place from the test scores x_i, we are at liberty to re-define their scales to suit ourselves. This is true, but is in effect assumed already done in the expansion (16); one cannot in general transform away the second-degree terms in (16) merely by changing the scales of f_1 and f_2.[1] As the quadratic terms f_1^2 and f_2^2 only arise in (16) if the separate scales of f_1 and f_2 are *changing* from test to test, the bi-linear or product factor $f_3 \equiv f_1 f_2$ would, at a guess, appear of more potential interest.

To discriminate such a factor from a genuine third factor, it would be necessary to examine its dependence on f_1 and f_2 over the population of persons; for example, the correlation between f_3 and the *product* of f_1 and f_2 would be, not zero, but unity (apart of course from sampling errors). Any such investigation would be somewhat complicated by the rotational arbitrariness of factors referred to earlier. Even if (16) simplified to

$$x_i = m_{i1} f_1 + m_{i2} f_2 + m_{i3} f_1 f_2 + m'_{i0} s'_i \qquad (18)$$

the factors f'_1, f'_2, f'_3 inferred would be some unknown orthogonal transformation of f_1, f_2 and f_3. Other genuine factors would further complicate

---

[1] Transforming any x_i to normality appears related to a suggestion by Professor Peel (13) for obtaining an absolute scale, but to reduce (16) to a linear model would require a mathematical transformation of the *simultaneous* distribution of all the x_i; since such a simultaneous transformation could give us pretty well anything we liked, it would not appear to have any particular relevance.

the issue. In spite of these difficulties, and although I would doubt whether any such possible non-linear effects would materially reduce the error of prognosis for individual persons, I should say a search for such effects would be worth-while, whether or not the results were positive.

References

(1) Bartlett, M. S. (1937) "The statistical conception of mental factors", *Brit. J. Psychol. (Gen. Sect.)* **28**, 97.

(2) —— (1937) "Note on the development of correlations among genetic components of ability", *Ann. Eugen.* **7**, 299.

(3) —— (1938) "Methods of estimating mental factors", *Nature*, **141**, 609.

(4) —— (1948) "Internal and external factor analysis", *Brit. J. Psychol. (Statist. Sect.)* **1**, 73.

(5) —— (1950) "Tests of significance in factor analysis", *Brit. J. Psychol. (Statist. Sect.)* **3**, 77.

(6) —— (1951) "A further note on tests of significance in factor analysis", *Brit. J. Psychol. (Statist. Sect.)* **4**, 1.

(7) Burt, C. (1940) "The factors of the mind" (Univ. of London Press, 1st ed.).

(8) —— (1949) "Alternative methods of factor analysis and their relations to Pearson's method of 'principal axes' ", *Brit. J. Phychol. (Statist. Sect.)* **2**, 98.

(9) Emmett, W. G. (1949) "Factor analysis by Lawley's method of maximum likelihood", *Brit. J. Psychol. (Statist. Sect.)* **2**, 90.

(10) Hayek, F. A. (1952) "The sensory order" (Routledge and Kegan Paul, London).

(11) Lawley, D. N. (1940) "The estimation of factor loadings by the method of maximum likelihood", *Proc. Roy. Soc. Edin.* **60**, 64.

(12) Kendall, M. G. (1950) "Factor analysis as a statistical technique", *J. Roy. Statist. Soc.* (Series B), **12**, 60.

(13) Peel, E. A. (1949) "Item difficulty as the measuring device in objective mental tests", *Brit. J. Psychol. (Statist. Sect.)* **2**, 69.

(14) Thomson, G. H. (1951) "The factorial analysis of human ability" (Univ. of London Press, 5th ed.).

(15) —— (1951) "Factor analysis, its hopes and dangers", *Proc. 13th Int. Cong. Psychol.* (Stockholm) 50.

(16) Thurstone, L. L. (1947) "Multiple factor analysis" (Chicago).

(17) Whittle, P. (1953) "On principal components and least square methods of factor analysis", *Skandinavisk Aktuarietidskrift* **35**, 223.

Stochastic Processes
or the Statistics of Change

What are Stochastic Processes ?

A few years ago not many people in this country knew what was meant by a stochastic process; today the situation is perhaps no different for the general public, though professional statisticians are becoming more familiar with the phrase. Like other new phrases or words, its use 'catches on,' and it gradually spreads through the community of statisticians or other receptive agents much in the way an actual infection will spread. Such a process is itself a *stochastic* process, by which is meant that it does not proceed according to any immutable law but is at least partly dependent on random and chance factors. We therefore call it a *random* or *stochastic* process, usually preferring the second adjective because *random* might convey the idea that every stochastic process appeared purely haphazard (like the emissions from a radioactive substance or the so-called Brownian motion of small dust particles on the surface of a liquid), whereas in many stochastic processes, such as the spread of epidemics or the growth of populations, any random fluctuations may be apparently eliminated by the large statistical groups involved, so that the development of the process appears comparatively smooth and even predetermined.

Anyone previously unfamiliar with the idea of a stochastic process will by now be beginning to see what is meant. He may, even if his mathematics is a relic from his schooldays, remember the distinction in mechanics between statics and dynamics. If he is an economist he will know that much of classical economic theory is erected on the same kind of static or equilibrium structure as classical statistical mechanics, and will know that modern economic theorists, like their physicist colleagues, are busy trying to formulate their theories to

---

* This article is based on a paper given at the Joint Conference of the Royal and Manchester Statistical Societies held in Manchester in September 1952.

represent a little more closely our dynamic changing world. If he is a statistician he will know that mathematical statisticians long ago began to study the statistical populations and frequency distributions arising in nature and how far they may be represented by theoretical models which assist in their interpretation. *The theory of stochastic processes is, roughly speaking, concerned with the corresponding wider theory of the statistics of change.*

Interpreting the subject in this way, we can be either excited by its generality or disappointed by its lack of novelty. Of course, stochastic processes have always been there in nature, and the industrial statistician studying his control charts or the commercial statistician his firm's fluctuating sales figures will not automatically solve his problems by calling them by a new name. However, while the statistician should never be hidebound by the standard techniques available to him, there is a limit to the extent to which even the best statistician can make *ad hoc* improvisations on current methods, and there is no doubt that recent systematic study of the theory of stochastic processes has greatly broadened his possible approach to actual statistical problems. I will cite two or three examples of how the older 'static' outlook tended to be a barrier to improved technique until it was broken down.

The first was in the statistical analysis of time-series.* The 'static' procedure of considering a given sample of *independent* observations had of course been adapted as far as possible to the study of time-series even in classical methods, in which the stochastic process was represented by a trend or a harmonic curve to which independent random fluctuations were supposed added; but even this assumption proved too narrow to cover many cases met with in practice. In particular, the impossibility of such an assumption always being feasible became apparent from the case of continuous time-records. In this case the assumption of independence implied unlimited statistical information if the discrete observations taken over a fixed period of time were increased indefinitely by reducing the interval between successive observations. Historically, the first attacks on this important statistical problem using a more general approach were made independently by the Russian mathematician and econometrician E. Slutsky[23] and by the English statistician Udny Yule[25] in the year 1927.

The second example was in the practice of industrial sampling. The 'single sampling' schemes were supplemented by 'double sampling,' 'inverse sampling,' and finally by the 'sequential sampling' methods, whose theory was mainly developed during the last world war by the American mathematical statistician Abraham Wald.[7] With these sequential methods the new feature is the *continuation* of sampling until enough information has been acquired for a decision to be taken with a specified risk. Sequential sampling is thus much less 'static' than the classical practice of taking a sample of predetermined size, and its

---

* This general heading strictly includes such topics as control charts, especially if the successive entries in the latter turn out to be correlated.

distributional theory (e.g. determining the average size of sample required in any application) is essentially one falling within the general field of stochastic process theory and, in particular, is related to the 'random walks' and diffusion processes referred to in the next section.

As a third example consider the manner in which discrete frequency distributions arise—in particular the well-known Poisson distribution for small numbers. In text-books this is usually derived from the binomial distribution, but a more direct and in many cases a more natural way is to obtain it as the fundamental distribution associated with events occurring randomly and independently of each other in time, such as the emission of alpha-particles by a radioactive substance or, in suitable cases, the occurrence of accidents to a particular individual or at a particular locality. The theoretical derivation is comparatively simple. If the total number of events occurring in the time t is $N(t)$, then the distribution of $N(t)$ can be specified by its 'probability-generating function'

$$G(z; t) \equiv p_0(t) + p_1(t)z + p_2(t)z^2 + \cdot \cdot \cdot,$$

in which the coefficient $p_r(t)$ of z^r is the probability that $N(t) = r$ after a time t. We suppose that in a small time-interval δt the chance of one extra event occurring is $a \, \delta t$ (for simplicity we assume a constant in time, though this is not essential), and the chance of none, $1 - a \, \delta t$. Then

$$G(z; t + \delta t) = a \, \delta t \, zG(z; t) + (1 - a \, \delta t)G(z; t)$$

or $$dG/dt = a(z - 1)G,$$

whence $$G = e^{at(z - 1)}$$

if $N(0) = 0$. This is the probability-generating function of the Poisson law $p_r(t) = e^{-m}m^r/r!$, with a mean $m = at$. The theory of stochastic processes thus gives the Poisson distribution a basic role in statistical theory not less than that of any other distribution.

Of course, if the events (e.g. accidents) are not independent the distribution may be modified. An important case is that where the chance of an event in the small time-interval δt is not constant, but depends on the number of events that have already occurred, being of the form $[a + bN(t)] \, \delta t$. This 'contagion' hypothesis may be shown by an extension of the above method to lead to the 'negative binomial distribution,' a result first established as long ago as 1914 by A. G. McKendrick,[4] who was interested in its medical applications. Another way in which this same distribution can arise was discovered in 1920 by Greenwood and Yule, who were investigating the numbers of accidents experienced by a group of munition workers. They found that if these workers were variable in their proneness to accidents then the frequency distribution of the numbers of accidents per individual, obtained from the statistics of the whole group, may be of the 'negative binomial' type (see, for example, Lundberg[3]). If we wish to discriminate between the first hypothesis, that any individual may suffer more accidents than the average because initial accidents contracted by bad luck render him more liable to others, and the second hypothesis, that one individual will differ from another in his accident proneness right from the start, it is necessary to analyse the accidents per individual over more than one time-period. This has recently been done, for example, on statistics collected for South African shunters.[1]

The fact that more than one causal mechanism can generate the same statistical distribution is an obvious warning to the statistician who is hoping to learn something of the way an observed distribution may have arisen. Before embarking on such a task he should ideally be familiar with *all* the theoretical possibilities. Even so, without some further limitation of the possible hypotheses, the extent to which he can unravel data presented to him may be severely limited. This difficult but vital problem of what the statistician is entitled to ask before undertaking a statistical analysis, particularly in connection with stochastic processes, is returned to again later.

The Monte Carlo Method

While systematic study of stochastic processes is recent, it is evident that in various guises they have appeared since the concepts of probability and chance were first formulated. It is in fact remarkable how the early mathematicians in their attacks on probability problems raised by gamblers included studies of game sequences closely related to many modern stochastic process problems, such as sequential analysis or the use of artificial stochastic processes to solve differential equations and other theoretical problems (the so-called 'Monte Carlo method'). For example, in 1657 the famous Dutch mathematician C. Huyghens propounded the following problem (quoted from a paper by Professor G. A. Barnard[17]). 'A and B each take twelve counters and play with three dice on this condition, that if eleven is thrown, A gives a counter to B, and if fourteen is thrown, B gives a counter to A; and he wins the game who first obtains all the counters. Show that A's chance is to B's as 244 140 625 is to 282 429 536 481.' The mathematical equation for this problem is readily set up; for if the chances of obtaining fourteen or eleven at any trial are as $p : q$ (actually 15 : 27 in this case), the probability $P(x)$ of A winning when he has x counters must satisfy the 'difference equation'

$$P(x) = \frac{p}{p+q} P(x+1) + \frac{q}{p+q} P(x-1), \ (0 < x < 24) \ldots.(1)$$

and also $P(0) = 0$, $P(24) = 1$. The relevant solution is

$$P(x) = [(q/p)^x - 1]/[(q/p)^{24} - 1] \qquad \ldots (2)$$

or in particular

$$P(12) = 1/[(q/p)^{12} + 1] \qquad \ldots (3)$$

agreeing with Huyghens's answer.

The interesting point about this is that, if the theoretical solution of the problem, which has been formulated in mathematical terms in equation (1), had not been precisely known, an approximate solution could be obtained not by direct numerical methods, but by repeated simulation of the gambling problem. As a simple illustration, one hundred repetitions were made, all of which resulted in A losing, consistently with the true value of P being as low as 0·000 864. To expedite these repetitions they were made for convenience with the aid of four-figure random numbers rather than of dice. To obtain odds of 15 : 27 we may classify any random number into one of the two groups 0000–3570 and 3571–9999, giving the practically equivalent odds 3571 : 6429. Notice how the artificial games, which simulate real ones, can give us at the same time all possible information we may wish to know. For example, we know the number of trials required before a game is terminated, and so accumulate information on the statistical distribution of the 'length' of a game. This problem can also be solved theoretically, but the mathematical solution is quite complicated.

This 'artificial sampling' or 'Monte Carlo method' is well known to statisticians, so much so that tables of random numbers are a familiar item in their libraries. In recent years, however, it has also been seriously considered by mathematicians as an aid to the solution of differential or other mathematical equations (see, for example, the USA publication on the 'Monte Carlo method'[10]). Thus the above gambling problem is an example of what is called a 'random walk' process in which each 'step' (in this case the transfer of a counter) occurs independently of previous steps; if we further consider the individual steps of this 'walk' to be small compared with the total distances to be traversed (in the gambling problem the number of counters originally held must be comparatively large), it may be shown that the density f of 'paths' when a large number of repetitions of the process is envisaged satisfies the partial differential equation

$$\partial f/\partial t + a\,\partial f/\partial x = b\,\partial^2 f/\partial x^2 \qquad \dots (4)$$

where x is the net distance traversed in the 'time' t (the number of steps), $a = (p - q)/(p + q)$, and $b = 2pq/(p + q)^2$. This equation is well known as the 'equation of diffusion' in physics, and conversely, if we met this equation directly and wished to obtain a solution of it by the Monte Carlo method, we could choose an appropriate $p : q$ (altering if necessary the scale of t and hence of a and b), and proceed as already indicated. Of course, we should be unlikely in this rather simple case to use this method in practice unless the boundary conditions were more complicated or we required to accumulate a lot of information simultaneously about the underlying process. However, to illustrate the connection with equation (4), the frequency distribution of the *lengths* of the 'games' in the hundred repetitions already referred to is compared in Fig. 1 with the theoretical distribution from (4) of the time required to reach a boundary at distance 12 units from the starting point. The agreement, with so few stages as 12 to reach the boundary in the artificial games, is surprisingly good.

It might be added that the reason a stochastic process may so often be found corresponding to equations arising in physics is the obvious one that the equation has really arisen in the first place, as in the case of equation (4), from a stochastic process occurring in nature.

Stochastic Processes in Physics and Communication Engineering

The reader will, however, appreciate that this more fundamental role of stochastic processes in physical problems cannot be adequately

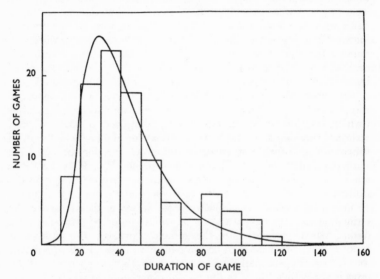

FIG. 1. Frequency distribution of the duration of play in 100 'games,' yielding an approximate solution of a diffusion problem whose correct solution is given by the continuous curve.

indicated here. It must suffice to remind him that the explicit use of the theory of stochastic processes for such physical phenomena as the showers of particles created by cosmic rays or other 'chain reactions,' as Brownian motion or other 'noise' phenomena, or as turbulence in gases and liquids, is merely one indication of the increasing necessity with all physical processes to allow fully for the role which chance and statistical concepts play in them.

Two topics may perhaps be singled out as of particular interest in industrial physics and communication engineering. The first is concerned with the stray disturbances in electrical and other delicate apparatus and has already been referred to above by its usual title, 'noise.' The problem of correcting and filtering a long train of signals to reduce the effect of noise to a minimum is one that comes under the general theory of what are called 'stationary' time-series, and has been so treated by Norbert Wiener, the American mathematician.[15] By a *stationary* time-series is meant a stochastic process in time in which the variable is fluctuating or oscillating but not otherwise changing as time goes on (an example is shown in Fig. 2). From the point of view of the communication engineer a continuing sequence of messages or signals may often be regarded as a stationary time-series, whether or not they are affected by external random disturbances. For example, in a long passage in English the way in which the various letters or even words happen to follow each other has a definite and constant statistical structure which can be studied. If someone sends such a passage by teleprinter or communicates it verbally by telephone, the resulting electrical signals will also constitute a stationary time-series.

The second topic is concerned with the *communication* and *coding* aspect of these series of messages or signals. It is clear that while the sequence of electrical signals should, apart from the effect of disturbances, represent the original sequences of messages, there is a considerable choice in how the representation is made; and one method may be better than another. Here again the concept of stationary time-series is used in the construction of a general theory of communication, in which are studied and made precise such questions as: what is the maximum rate of information that may be passed along a given channel, or equivalently, how 'big' has a channel to be to pass a required rate of information? To give some idea, to those familiar with the technical jargon of the electrical engineer, of the kind of results that can be reached, I will merely quote one important result. The maximum 'capacity' of a channel under certain conditions is given by the formula

$$W \log (1 + P/N)$$

where W is the band-width of frequencies employed, N is the average power in this band-width of the noise in the channel, and P the corresponding average power allowed in the signals. The efficiency of actual communication systems, for example those making use of frequency modulation in radio communication, can then be compared with this optimum.

This communication theory has been largely developed by workers at the Bell Telephone Laboratories, especially by C. Shannon.[13] It is quite general and is not confined to electrical methods of communication. A symposium[14] was held in London in 1950 to discuss its numerous ramifications and several statisticians attended who were interested in its important relation with other branches of statistical theory (see also Barnard[11]).

Stochastic Processes in Industry

An older problem in communication engineering associated with the theory of stochastic processes arises, say, in the design of telephone switchboards and is the one of determining 'waiting times' for any given capacity and density of 'traffic.' But this has so many guises that it is better thought of in the more general terminology of the problem of 'queues,' which the inimitable periodical *Punch* evidently considered (from its review of Mr D. G. Kendall's paper[2]) to be one of the universal problems of our time. Whether the wait is for a disengaged line, or a disengaged shop assistant, or a vacant landing strip at an aerodrome, or a vacant gap in the road traffic, or an available operative to attend to a machine, the wait loses time and money, not to mention our patience. A theoretical and practical study of the stochastic processes involved may help to reduce the amount of time lost.

As an example consider the problem of servicing machines which break down at random times at an average rate r per machine. It is evident that a single group of n operatives to nN machines will be, at least in the absence of any other practical considerations, more efficient than n separate operatives each servicing a separate group of N machines, because the possibility of an operative to one of the latter groups being idle while a machine in another group requires attention is excluded when all operatives are pooled. To illustrate the gain in more detail in a particular case, suppose that the time taken to finish servicing any machine once it has received attention is also random with an average S. Also for simplicity in this example we shall suppose that N is large, but that the average rate of breakdown for all machines remains at a reasonable figure R, say, $(= Nr)$. It might be noticed that our problem is now theoretically equivalent to a queue problem with customers coming in at random to be served, with the operatives representing servers.

The average number of machines (customers) waiting to be served comes out in the case $n = 1$ (one server) as $a^2/(1 - a)$ per server, where $a = RS$, whereas for $n = 2$ it is $2a^3/(1 - a^2)$. Thus the ratio of the average number waiting in the second case to twice the average number for one server is $a/(1 + a)$, indicating the gain in efficiency already referred to. For a, which must be less than 1 if stable conditions are to be maintained, equal to $\frac{1}{2}$ we have $2a^2/(1 - a) = 1$, $2a^3/(1 - a^2) = \frac{1}{3}$, and the gain ratio is as much as $3 : 1$. As n further increases the ratio of the expected number of waiting machines to the total expected number in n individual groups with one operative per group tends steadily to zero. This example has, of course, been rather drastically simplified for illustrative purposes, and statisticians interested in this problem should consult a more comprehensive discussion by F. Benson and D. R. Cox.[18]

Apart from the connection already noted of sequential sampling theory with stochastic processes, many sampling problems have been reconsidered in recent years from the stochastic process viewpoint. Thus the problem of sampling from a continuous 'flow' of material has been discussed by G. H. Jowett[20] and the problem of sampling a two-dimensional area (using the idea of a stochastic process over two *spatial* dimensions) by M. H. Quenouille.[5]

It is clearly not only in the *sampling* of a continuous output of some material that a knowledge of stochastic processes may be useful; it will be needed in the statistical analysis and quality control of the material. For example, in the textile industry, whether for cotton, wool, flax, or other fibre, considerable attention has been given to maintaining uniform quality of the yarn. In particular, certain tendencies to periodicity in the thickness of cotton 'slivers' before they are spun into yarn were discussed by G. A. R. Foster at a symposium[24] on time-series held in 1946. It has already been mentioned that a new approach

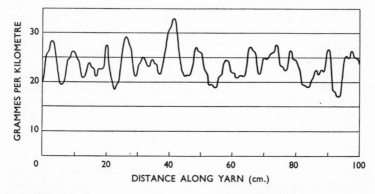

FIG. 2. This chart shows the variation in mass per unit length along a cotton yarn. It was kindly supplied by Mr G. A. R. Foster, who has dealt elsewhere[19,24] with the analysis of such variation. The form of the variation is typical of that shown by a stationary time-series.

to time-series in the last twenty-five years has enabled us to attack such problems statistically with a much greater understanding of what methods to employ.

The Analysis of Economic and Other Time-Series

I have given a technical survey of the statistical analysis of time-series elsewhere[14] and do not want to attempt it here; I do, however, without going into technicalities want to emphasise that the extent to which the statistician can hope to analyse time-series by purely em-pirical means is now realised to be severely limited. This is because any analysis depends on a theoretical specification or hypothesis of how the data have arisen, and the less detailed the specification avail-able the fewer the conclusions that can be drawn. This is sometimes forgotten in classical statistical problems, where the assumption of a sample of *independent* and *homogeneous* observations is so common that it is often not mentioned explicitly. As an exception, in many experi-mental situations the lack of independence was not only recognised, but it was effectively eliminated by the randomisation devices intro-duced by Sir Ronald Fisher. But in time-series, and indeed in stochastic processes in general, the dependence between the successive observations is usually their most important feature. This has thrown up many new and difficult problems in the theory of statistical inference. However, even when these purely technical problems have been solved, it is necessary to realise that the nature of the dependence has so many possibilities *a priori* that these need first to be drastically restricted in any particular context by theoretical or other sources of information before any analysis is likely to be profitable. Possible exceptions are time-series of the stationary type occurring in some physical or meteorological applications, where the length of series available for study may be more or less unlimited.

In economic and social studies it is rare to have homogeneous series of any length, and any statistical analysis must be closely knit with as full a theoretical specification as possible. Referring especially to this field, Norbert Wiener[16] has made much the same point (p. 35): '. . . the modern apparatus of the theory of small samples, once it goes beyond the determination of its own specially defined parameters and becomes a method for positive statistical inference in new cases, does not inspire one with any confidence, unless it is applied by a statistician by whom the main elements of the dynamics of the situation are either explicitly known or implicitly felt.'

The statistical analysis of economic time-series has thus in recent years been based on rather well-defined hypothetical models of how the variables under study interact with one another. When Udny Yule introduced in 1927 methods of analysis for oscillatory time-series in which the random or stochastic element became incorporated with the future movement of the series, he used the vivid illustration of a swinging pendulum which was being bombarded by boys armed with peashooters. It is not unreasonable to suppose that any random or unpredictable disturbances affecting economic series similarly influence their future movement, and so the theoretical economic models used in the specification automatically become stochastic processes of the kind considered by Yule. One detailed (though somewhat indigestible !) exposition[21] of the statistical methods developed for analysing such types of stochastic series has been published by the Cowles Commission Economic Research Group at Chicago.

Stochastic Processes and the Statistician's Role

The essentially close relation between theory and statistical analysis in the case of economic time-series rather brings to a head the problem of what responsibility devolves on anyone who undertakes statistical analysis. It has always been stressed that the statistician must be fully cognisant of how the figures he is analysing were collected and of any other relevant information, but in the case of stochastic processes it is clear that this ancillary information should also include a very thorough theoretical knowledge of the possible mechanism and structure of the process before any analysis can proceed. We have seen that stochastic processes may arise in any field of application, and any statistician who finds himself responsible for their analysis must be prepared either to acquire such knowledge himself or to co-operate with someone who has it.

Let us consider an example in the actuarial field, the prediction of population trends. Here it is true that any random or stochastic element affecting separate individuals is practically eliminated if it is the total population size that is of interest. But while the process will appear smooth, its *detailed structure* is a determining factor in its evolution, and it is well known that any empirical extrapolation based on the census figures for the total population is quite inadequate for any but short-term purposes. This is most evident if we consider as an extreme case a fictitious population of young married emigrants who have founded an island colony. The island's birth-rate would at first show large but gradually damped oscillations with a period of about one generation, until the successive generations had had time to merge into each other. Thus more extended extrapolations before the war took full account of (i) the distribution by age and sex of the total population and (ii) fertility and death rates for individual ages. Even this, which it will be noticed takes account of the *instantaneous* detailed structure of the population of individuals, has been recently shown to be insufficient, for it is necessary to recognise the growing custom of planning family size, and hence to try to follow family histories.[22]

Even when random fluctuations are neglected it is worth remembering that they are still there, and that with smaller groups such as some animal populations they may become a crucial factor. Populations are examples of what are called multiplicative stochastic processes, for which fluctuations are cumulative in time. *In appraising the possible size of random fluctuations the statistician must therefore use the theory of fluctuations appropriate to the relevant stochastic process, and this may sometimes be quite different from the 'classical' theory of fluctuations.* Thus for populations with an expected balance of births and deaths relative fluctuations will theoretically tend to be of order $\sqrt{(t/n)}$, in contrast with the classical formula $\sqrt{(1/n)}$, where t is the time in generations and n the mean size of population. For a human population of 50 000 000 and a generation time of, say, 30 years, this is still only of order 1/5 000 after 60 years; but for an animal population of 100 with a generation time of one year it is of order 1/3 after 10 years.

Stochastic Processes in Biology

This theory of population fluctuations is linked with a problem first raised by Francis Galton at the end of the last century in connection with the extinction of family surnames: if each male individual in a population independently has a family containing n sons, where n is a random number following some given distribution, and the sons in turn each have a number of sons following the same distribution, what is the chance of any particular male line becoming extinct? The complete solution, first obtained by J. F. Steffensen, is a peculiar one. Suppose the probability-generating function of the distribution of n is

$$G(z) = p_0 + p_1 z + p_2 z^2 + \cdots,$$

the probability that $n = r$ being the coefficient p_r of z^r in $G(z)$. Then provided that $p_0 \neq 0$ (otherwise it is obvious that extinction could not occur), the chance of ultimate extinction is the smallest root z_0 of the equation

$$G(z) = z.$$

Moreover, this root z_0 is unity unless the average n is *greater* than unity; even for the United States population in 1920, when the average value of n was 1·145, it was shown by the American actuary Lotka from the statistics of family sizes that the chance of extinction was still nearly 0·9. For example, if for $G(z)$ he substituted the approximate expression $(0·482 - 0·041z)/(1 - 0·559z)$ the above equation became the quadratic equation

$$0·482 - 1·041z + 0·559z^2 = (1 - z)(0·482 - 0·559z) = 0,$$

giving $z_0 = 0·482/0·559 = 0·86$.

This extinction problem* is important also in the theory of natural selection, since n may alternatively be interpreted as the number of mutant genes in one generation stemming from a mutant gene in the last; as it is unlikely that even a favourable mutation will give an average n much above unity, it will require many occurrences of any such mutation before it is likely to become firmly established in the population. [27]

This last application reminds us that, since the theory of fluctuations in populations is specially important for small populations, it is particularly relevant to all biological population problems involving occasional mutations—the mutant individuals form at first a small population however large the rest of the population may be.

A recent application of the theory of stochastic processes has been to the study of fluctuations in bacterial populations. When the normal bacterial type is placed in an unfavourable environment (for example, a nutrient medium impregnated with bacteriophage) it is possible that a mutant type will arise resistant to this environment. An alternative hypothesis advanced by Sir Cyril Hinshelwood to account for the survival of the bacteria in the new environment is that an actual adaptation of the organism to the environment may lead to survival. Whichever theory may be the correct one (and the latest evidence suggests that neither theory alone is likely to be applicable to all

---

* For further historical references to this problem see D. G. Kendall's paper 'Stochastic Processes and Population Growth.' [6] The ubiquity of the extinction problem is also indicated (i) by its identification with the gambler's 'ruin' in the historical problems referred to early in this article, and (ii) by its relevance for the epidemiological model treated in the next section.

situations), a study and comparison with observation of the postulated mechanism of growth is evidently necessary. This has been attempted for the mutation theory, and a recent survey is given by Dr P. Armitage.[26]

Stochastic Processes in Medicine

So far I have been taking very much a 'bird's-eye view' of stochastic processes in relation to statistics, and the reader can justifiably complain that the references to applications have been too brief to be other than tantalising. Stochastic processes appear in many branches of medicine also, for example in the study of nervous and cerebral activity or in the study of possible mechanisms of carcinogenesis (see papers by Mc-Culloch & Pitts,[31] and Iverson & Arley[30]). It may, however, be more helpful if I conclude with a single example from the medical field treated in somewhat greater detail. In the discussion following an admirable survey of statistical problems in medicine given at the 1951 Cambridge Conference of the Royal Statistical Society by N. T. J. Bailey[28] I mentioned the probable value of the 'Monte Carlo method' in epidemiological theory. We have seen that it is possible in the growth of very large populations to neglect the stochastic element, but if we do so for epidemics of infectious diseases, especially those whose incidence in the population exhibits a quasi-periodic character, I believe we are in danger of omitting an important factor in their theoretical mechanism.

As an illustration I shall describe the results obtained in a series of fictitious 'measles epidemics,' generated with the aid of random numbers, under conditions simulating a partially isolated group such as a boarding-school. Measles, although not usually a serious complaint, is a favourite infectious disease for study among epidemiologists owing to its relatively simple epidemic character; it confers permanent immunity among almost all those attacked, who are mostly children under the age of 15 (a useful summary of the epidemiology of measles may be found in the late Professor Greenwood's study of epidemics[29]). Notifications are known to exhibit two comparatively stable statistical features. The first is a tendency to biennial periodicity; for example, for Manchester for the years 1917–51 this tendency is quite marked. The second is a seasonal variation; in the case of Manchester for the same years this ranged from 60 per cent. above the average at the beginning of a calendar year to 60 per cent. below in the late summer. It is, however, not at all easy to reconcile these two statistical facts. One may investigate the theoretical consequences of a simple model in which 'susceptibles,' i.e. children who have not yet contracted measles, come in at a given rate and run a risk of infection proportional to the number of infected children present. This model was first shown by Sir William Hamer and later by H. E. Soper[29, 33] to be sufficient to produce epidemic waves with a period in time of the right order of magnitude. Unfortunately, in contradiction to what is observed, these waves damp down until an endemic steady state of infection is reached. If we introduce a seasonal variation in infectivity, a 10 per cent. variation is amply sufficient to produce the observed seasonal variation in notifications; it may be shown that the corresponding theoretical variation in numbers of infected comes out at about 80 per cent. But the seasonal variation forces its own annual period on the waves, and the longer natural period, which corresponds to the observed period, still disappears. Dr Soper believed that the introduction of a definite incubation period of a fortnight counteracted the damping effect but, as first pointed out by E. B. Wilson and J. Worcester[35], he was misled by an inaccurate numerical method. From a study of the transmission of infection in individual households Dr P. Stocks and Miss Mary Karn were led to the hypothesis that some of the children exposed to risk acquire a temporary immunity for about a year without visible contraction of the disease, and suggested that this could contribute to the biennial periodic tendency by protecting unattacked children during the danger period of the following year. But this amended model does not appear on theoretical examination to eliminate the difficulty, and I have begun to suspect that a way out from the dilemma must introduce rather different ideas.

The common feature of the calculations on all these models has up to recently been their straightforward actuarial basis, with no attempt to incorporate the random or stochastic element. I shall refer to such models as 'deterministic' models. But it may prove necessary to recognise the essentially local and hence stochastic nature of infection (random overall variation in infectivity due to weather, etc., will of course also contribute), and on such a new basis continual 'extinction' and replenishment of infected individuals within small groups may create a statistical balance with the damping tendency. In other words, the endemic steady state cannot be attained because it is *stochastically* unstable. To investigate this hypothesis for, say, an entire city is a tall order, for it means studying the stochastic vicissitudes of infections in our theoretical model, which must first be expanded to cover adequately the geographical grouping. It is hoped in due course to carry out such an investigation with the aid of the electronic computer, but in the meantime I have compromised by investigating the similar but simpler problem for a fictitious boarding-school, which is treated as an effectively isolated group of children apart from the influx of children at the beginning of each term.

The precise conditions assumed for the stochastic model are as follows:

(i) *Influx of Susceptibles.*

'Lent term' (1st week)	.. ..	7
'Summer term' (18th week) ..	..	7
'Christmas term' (36th week)	..	23

The numbers are intended to represent a typical case, with much the greatest influx at the beginning of the school year. It should be noted that immune children are to be ignored.

(ii) *Influx of Infectives.* The entry of infection is assumed to occur by an occasional one or two incoming susceptibles being already infected; the actual number for any term is random, following a Poisson frequency law, for convenience cut off at the value 3. The mean of this distribution is taken proportional to the number of new entrants, but some provisional assumption is also necessary about the seasonal proportion of infectives in the population from which these new entrants are drawn. It seems reasonable, in the absence of a complete stochastic theory for the population outside the school, to base this on the annual oscillations in numbers which follow, as already noted, from an assumed seasonal variation in infectivity on the *deterministic* model. However, it will be seen that the precise assumptions made about the entry of infection are not very crucial provided that some new infection is present from time to time. In the real situation the children would of course not be completely isolated from the rest of the community during term. Moreover, the actual dispersal of the children in the vacations may not only introduce infection through these children but will effectively terminate school epidemics at the end of each term. In the model the vacations are entirely ignored.

(iii) *Infectivity.* The average infection rate per susceptible is assumed to be $\lambda_r = 0 \cdot 01 [1 + 0 \cdot 1 \cos (2\pi r/52)]$ per infected person per week, where r is the number of the week in the calendar year, 1st, 2nd, . . ., 52nd. This gives a maximum seasonal infectivity of 10 per cent. above the average at the beginning of the calendar year, and a minimum of 10 per cent. below the average in the middle of the year. The coefficient $0 \cdot 01$ corresponds roughly to the value $1/300\ 000$ originally adopted by Hamer and Soper, based on rates for the increase in numbers of susceptibles and incidence of infection for the whole of London. Its value has been scaled by a factor of $3\ 000$ to be consistent with the very much smaller group represented by a single school, the average number of susceptibles being taken of the order 50 instead of $150\ 000$. This leaves unaltered the approximate period of one and a half years for the gradually damped-out oscillations which follow an initial major epidemic in the deterministic model.

In the stochastic model the chance of infection in a small time-interval δt is taken to be $\lambda_r N_t S_t \, \delta t$, where N_t is the number of infectious children at any time t (measured in weeks), and S_t the number of children susceptible to attack.

(iv) *Recovery.* The chance of 'recovery,' by which is meant rather non-infectivity, corresponds to an average infectivity period of a fortnight. For simplicity it is assumed that the chance of recovery per interval δt is $\frac{1}{2}\delta t$, and that an infected child is infectious all the time until such recovery. The actual situation is more complicated; for instance, part at least of the incubation period of about a fortnight is non-infectious and this appears to lead in some local measles epidemics to a fortnightly periodic structure at the beginning of the epidemic; but we cannot expect any such 'fine-structure' phenomena to appear in our rather crude model. However, it is emphasised that the primary object of the investigation is to examine the self-consistency and possible broad appropriateness of the model; the above oversimplified pattern of infection and recovery actually exaggerates, by a factor of about 2, the damping of the epidemic waves in the deterministic model, but this will not prejudice its relevance if, as in fact is the case, the damping is eliminated in the stochastic model.

(v) *Initial Conditions.* An initial 'epidemic' was started with 100 susceptibles and 5 infectives, these rather arbitrary numbers ensuring, with the high chance of about 0·97, that the artificial series began with a major epidemic.

Complete details of the calculations will not be given, but the way in which they were made can perhaps be indicated. With a process or model developing continuously in time two methods of obtaining artificial realisations of it are possible. With the first, the time is divided up into small intervals and an approximate model proceeding in terms of these small steps is used. This was the method by which the random walk process referred to under the 'Monte Carlo method' could be used to obtain an approximate solution of the diffusion equation, although this equation represents a *continuous* diffusion of particles. This method is not very convenient for the epidemiological problem, for events such as infections multiply rapidly when an epidemic is under way and may be few and far between in the quiescent periods between epidemics. We want in effect our time-scale much finer during an epidemic than at other times. It is therefore more convenient to adopt the second method, in which we determine the random interval between two consecutive events rather than the number of events in a given interval (cf. reference[9]).

Thus the chance of an 'event' in a small interval δt on the above assumptions is

$$a \, \delta t \equiv \lambda_r N_t S_t \, \delta t + \tfrac{1}{2} N_t \, \delta t$$

where the first term on the right represents the chance of a new infection and the second the chance that the infectives drop by one. The coefficient λ_r changes only slowly with time and may be treated as temporally constant. N_t and S_t, apart from the influx at the beginning of terms, cannot by definition change until the next 'event' has occurred, and hence the coefficient a is effectively constant. It follows from the theory developed earlier in this article that the chance that no event occurs in the interval t is the initial probability in a Poisson distribution with mean at, viz. e^{-at}. This defines the so-called 'exponential distribution' for the interval before a further event occurs, and if we write $T = at$, it will be seen that the distribution of the standardised interval T on this adjusted time-scale is independent of a. We may thus choose a random interval T by some convenient method, and then convert back to the real time scale t by writing $t = T/a$. The method actually used to obtain random intervals was to take $T = \frac{1}{2}(X^2 + Y^2)$, where X and Y are random standardised normal or Gaussian variables available in published tables, but any other method of obtaining a random quantity following the exponential distribution will of course do equally well. At the end of the interval $t = T/a$ we still have to decide *which* event has occurred, but since the relative odds of a new infection and a recovery are $\lambda_r S_t N_t : \frac{1}{2} N_t = 2\lambda_r S_t : 1$, we can write $p = (2\lambda_r S_t)/(1 + 2\lambda_r S_t)$ and from reference to a table of ordinary random numbers decide whether the event that has occurred is a new infection. If it is, N_t goes up by one and S_t down by one; if it is not, N_t goes down by one and S_t up by one.

A further slight approximation is made at the beginning of each term when, if the last interval goes past this date when conditions change, it is ignored and calculations made afresh from this date with the new conditions. If at any stage N_t drops to zero, no change can of course occur until a new influx of children occurs.

The start of the calculations is shown in Table I covering the first week, for which $\lambda_r = 0.011\,00$. The coefficient λ_r used is that pertaining at the beginning of each week, and it is not changed until the next week is reached. The number of new cases during the week is the decrease in the number of susceptibles, viz. 7.

TABLE I

Random Interval T	a	T/a	p	Random Number	t (weeks)	N_t	S_t
	8·000				0	5	100
1·291 25		0·161	0·688	2952			
	9·534				0·161	6	99
0·077 45		0·008	0·685	4167			
	11·046				0·169	7	98
6·223 40		0·563	0·683	2730			
	12·536				0·732	8	97
0·547 85		0·044	0·681	0560			
	14·004				0·776	9	96
0·210 85		0·015	0·679	2754			
	15·450				0·791	10	95
0·370 00		0·024	0·676	5870			
	16·874				0·815	11	94
0·000 50		0·000	0·674	9268			
	15·340				0·815	10	94
0·276 25		0·018	0·674	2002			
	16·753				0·833	11	93
0·648 65		0·039	0·672	9568			
	15·230				0·872	10	93
2·645 45		0·174	0·672	8243			
					1·046	9	93

By such calculations the mock epidemic series was generated continuously for a total 'time' of 13 years, during which six major outbreaks were obtained with an average period between these epidemics of 125 weeks. The series was evidently 'steady' in the stochastic sense, with the last epidemics comparable in magnitude with the first. In addition there were four minor outbreaks, in which the entry of infection led to fresh cases but did not lead to a serious epidemic. The results are summarised in Table II, and the course of the largest epidemic (the fifth major epidemic) is shown in Fig. 3. It is stressed that these results are not intended in any sense as a 'fit' to observed data, but statistics for actual measles epidemics in boarding-schools[32] appear to have many similar features if we bear in mind all the further possible complications we have ignored in our model.

TABLE II
Mock epidemic series—summary table

Outbreak	Beginning in Week:	Total Notifications	Percentage Susceptibles Attacked
Major Epidemic			
1	1	98	87
2	105	72	83
3	244	88	85
4	365	67	76
5	504	117	91
6	625	74	87
Minor Outbreak			
1	140	7	18
2	226	7	8
3	556	6	14
4	660	5	15

(On eight other occasions infection entered the 'school' but did not lead to any fresh cases.)

The observed attack rate of presumed susceptibles in all the schools ranged up to 77 per cent. with, however, not such a clear distinction between major and minor outbreaks. (The actual seasonal incidence in the five years covered by the MRC Report[32] seems specially anomalous, with a higher incidence in the summer term than expected from the average in the population at large or in the corresponding mock series. But here it is again stressed that the extent to which the observed statistics can deviate from the average depends on the mechanism producing them, and for only a five-year period, especially as the incidence in different schools is likely to be correlated, considerable fluctuations would be possible.)

To conclude, while it is certainly not claimed that the mechanism of this simple model is sufficient to explain all the observed facts, it is hoped that this investigation will at least indicate the value of stochastic process models in epidemiological theory. In particular its results, which may be supported by theoretical argument, clearly demonstrate the possibility of a statistical balance between 'extinction' of infectives in a local group and fresh infection from outside. The period will partly depend on the 'isolation' of the local group, but in any case *a major epidemic cannot occur until the concentration of susceptibles has passed*

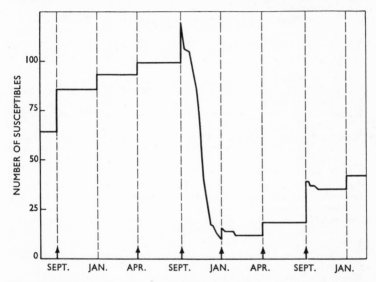

FIG. 3. Extract from mock epidemic series. This graph shows a major epidemic beginning in the autumn of the second 'school' year shown and ending in the New Year. A minor outbreak also occurs the following autumn. The dotted lines indicate the beginning of terms, when there are a number of new entrants to the school; the arrows indicate dates when infection also entered.

its critical threshold value. This critical density of susceptibles is not altogether a new notion to epidemiologists but it is suggested that only with the stochastic approach, in which a smaller density ensures local extinction, can it acquire proper theoretical justification.

I am greatly indebted to Mrs A. Linnert for carrying out the detailed computation for the artificial epidemic series.

REFERENCES AND BIBLIOGRAPHY

This short list of papers and books is confined mainly to applications referred to in the text. For the convenience of readers it has been classified according to the field of application, though this necessitates some cross-referencing. Many further references will of course be found in these publications.

I. *General*

[1] ARBOUS, A. G., & KERRICH, J. E. (1951). 'Accident Statistics and the Concept of Accident Proneness,' *Biometrics*, **7**, 340.

[2] KENDALL, D. G. (1951). 'Some Problems in the Theory of Queues,' *J. Roy. Statist. Soc.* B, **13**, 151.

[3] LUNDBERG, O. (1940). *On Random Processes and their Application to Sickness and Accident Statistics.* Almqvist & Wiksells, Uppsala.

[4] McKENDRICK, A. G. (1914). 'Studies on the Theory of Continuous Probabilities, with Special Reference to its Bearing on Natural Phenomena of a Progressive Nature,' *Proc. Lond. Math. Soc.* (2), **13**, 401.

[5] QUENOUILLE, M. H. (1949). 'Problems in Plane Sampling,' *Ann. Math. Statist.*, **20**, 355.

[6] SYMPOSIUM ON STOCHASTIC PROCESSES (1949). *J. Roy. Statist. Soc.* B, **11**, 150.

[7] WALD, A. (1947). *Sequential Analysis.* John Wiley, New York.

II. *Monte Carlo Method*

[8] HAMMERSLEY, J. M. (1950). 'Electronic Computers and the Analysis of Stochastic Processes,' *Math. Tables and Other Aids to Comp.*, **4**, No. 29, 56.

[9] KENDALL, D. G. (1950). 'An Artificial Realisation of a Simple "Birth-and-Death" Process,' *J. Roy. Statist. Soc.* B, **12**, 116.

[10] NATIONAL BUREAU OF STANDARDS (1951). *Monte Carlo Method*, Applied Mathematics Series, **12**. Washington, DC.

III. *Physics and Communication Engineering*

[11] BARNARD, G. A. (1951). 'The Theory of Information,' *J. Roy. Statist. Soc.* B, **13**, 66.

[12] CHANDRASEKHAR, S. (1943). 'Stochastic Problems in Physics and Astronomy,' *Reviews of Modern Physics*, **15**, 1.

[13] SHANNON, C. E., & WEAVER, W. (1949). *A Mathematical Theory of Communication*, University of Illinois Press, Urbana.

[14] SYMPOSIUM ON INFORMATION THEORY (1950). Ministry of Supply, London.

[15] WIENER, N. (1949). *The Extrapolation, Interpolation and Smoothing of Stationary Time-series, with Engineering Applications.* John Wiley, New York.

[16] *Idem.* (1948). *Cybernetics.* John Wiley, New York.

IV. *Industry* (See also I[1,2,3,5,7])

[17] BARNARD, G. A. (1946). 'Sequential Tests in Industrial Statistics,' *J. Roy. Statist. Soc.* B, **8**, 1.

[18] BENSON, F., & COX, D. R. (1951). 'The Productivity of Machines requiring Attention at Random Intervals,' *J. Roy. Statist. Soc.* B, **13**, 65.

[19] FOSTER, G. A. R. (1951). 'Fibre Motion in Roller Drafting,' *Shirley Inst. Mem.*, **25**, 51, and *J. Text. Inst.*, **42**, T335.

[20] JOWETT, G. H. (1952). 'The Accuracy of Systematic Sampling from Conveyor Belts,' *Applied Statistics*, **1**, 50.

V. *Analysis of Economic and Other Time-Series* (See also III[14,15,16] and IV[19])

[21] KOOPMANS, T. C. (editor) (1950). *Statistical Inference in Dynamic Economic Models.* John Wiley, New York.

[22] *Report of the Royal Commission on Population* (1949). HMSO, London.

[23] SLUTSKY, E. (1927). 'The Summation of Random Causes as the Source of Cyclic Processes,' *Problems of Economic Conditions*, ed. by the Conjuncture Institute, Moscow, **3**, No. 1 (later reprinted in *Econometrica*, **5** (1937), 105).

[24] SYMPOSIUM ON AUTOCORRELATION IN TIME-SERIES (1946). *J. Roy. Statist. Soc.* B, **8**, 27.

[25] YULE, G. U. (1927). 'On a Method of Investigating Periodicities in Disturbed Series, with special reference to Wolfer's Sun-spot Numbers,' *Philos. Trans.* A, **226**, 267.

VI. *Biology* (See also I[4,5,6] and VII)

[26] ARMITAGE, P. (1952). 'The Statistical Theory of Bacterial Populations subject to Mutation,' *J. Roy. Statist. Soc. B*, **14**, 1.
[27] FISHER, R. A. (1930). *The Genetical Theory of Natural Selection.* Oxford University Press.

VII. *Medicine*

[28] BAILEY, N. T. J. (1952). 'The Scope of Medical Statistics,' *Applied Statistics*, **I**, 149.
[29] GREENWOOD, MAJOR (1935). *Epidemics and Crowd Diseases.* Williams & Norgate, London.
[30] IVERSEN, S., & ARLEY, N. (1950). 'On the Mechanism of Experimental Carcinogenesis,' *Act. Path. and Microbiol. Scand.*, **27**, Fasc. 5, 773.
[31] McCULLOCH, W. S., & PITTS, W. (1948). 'The Statistical Organisation of Nervous Activity,' *Biometrics*, **4**, 91.
[32] MEDICAL RESEARCH COUNCIL (1950). *Epidemics in Schools*, Special Report No. 271, HMSO, London.
[33] SOPER, H. E. (1929). 'The Interpretation of Periodicity in Disease Prevalence,' *J. Roy. Statist. Soc.*, **92**, 34.
[34] WELCH, J. D., & BAILEY, N. T. J. (1952). 'Appointment Systems in Hospital Outpatient Departments,' *Lancet*, **I**, 1105.
[35] WILSON, E. B., & WORCESTER, J. (1945). 'Damping of Epidemic Waves' and 'The Spread of an Epidemic,' *Proc. Nat. Acad. Sci. Wash.*, **31**, 294 and 327.

The Statistical Analysis of Stochastic Processes

1. GENERAL REMARKS AND PRINCIPLES

Stationary time-series are the stochastic processes which have received most systematic attention from statisticians, but the problem of statistical inference for stochastic processes is, as Grenander (1950) has stressed, a general one which has nevertheless not until recently received much consideration. Grenander, in his important paper, was mostly concerned with extending the more classical apparatus of statistical inference to cover stochastic processes, especially those involving a continuous time-parameter. I shall come back to this work, but first I think it is useful to look at the problem more from the point of view of the practical statistician, and to examine some of the new difficulties which the statistical analysis of stochastic processes raises. Some discussion from this point of view I have included in a forthcoming book (Bartlett, 1955a, Ch. 8), and I may perhaps be allowed to quote the opening passage:

"The statistical analysis of stochastic processes arising in nature does not differ in principle from the analysis of other types of statistical data, but the existence of some dependence or continuity in the successive observations will often mean that the classical methods become inadequate, and need extension. Moreover, there are repercussions on the practical side, for unless the statistician has a well-defined and realistic model of the actual process he is studying, his analysis is likely to be abortive.

It is of course true that a statistician must always be fully cognisant of how his data were collected and of any other relevant information, but in the case of stochastic processes this ancillary information should certainly include as thorough a theoretical knowledge of the mechanism and structure of the process as possible. This is largely because dependence has so many more possibilities *a priori* than independence that these will usually need to be drastically restricted in any particular context."

Of course, when we survey the different types of data that may arise, some types may be analysable by classical methods. Two important cases are:

(i) the purely random sequence of independent events, with perhaps a systematic trend or periodic component super-imposed;

(ii) *independent* repetitions of the same process, of which isolated features are under test.

Some vital reservations are, however, necessary, and may be illustrated by examples. In case (i), it must be assumed that all that is being estimated or tested is the size or character of the systematic component, the independence of the observations for the purely random component not being in question. Thus the classical periodogram test of significance of a harmonic component with particular frequency becomes invalid if the class of alternatives includes time-series with an auto-regressive structure. As another example, a test of random-ness of a random sequence involving an examination of order will belong to the class of tests developed for dependent sequences; in particular, if the number of possible states is finite, the problem becomes one in the analysis of probability chains (Bartlett, 1950b).

An example of case (ii) are replicate growth cultures of bacteria subject to mutation; the replicates are separately transferred to nutrient medium impregnated with bacterio-phage, where only the mutant bacteria survive. The fluc-tuations in counts of mutant bacteria between replicates are not of course Poissonian, for the appropriate stochastic pro-cess theory must be used, and this may be shown (see, for example, Armitage, 1951) to lead to very large variation in the counts. However, in spite of the non-classical nature of this variability, the data to be analysed consist of a number of independent observations from a population which is theo-retically known on any particular theoretical model, and hence may be tested by the standard χ^2 test. The estimation of the parameters of the distribution, the most important of which involves the mutation-rate, also conforms to 'classical' methods.

This last example is no different in principle from the case of a homogeneous sample of observations, each one on a different individual, of the total number of accidents experienced in a given period. If the occurrence of accidents were purely random, the fluctuations in numbers would be Poissonian, but if the chance of an accident to a particular individual depends linearly on the number already experienced, then it is known that the numbers of accidents follow a negative binomial distribution. I have referred to this case because it is well-known that the negative binomial distribution can also be generated if the accident-rate per individual remains uniform, but if further the rate varies from individual to individual according to a χ^2 distribution. This emphasizes that the examination of isolated variables may be insufficient to distinguish possible alternative hypotheses, and naturally for any involving assumptions about the relation of numbers of accidents in successive intervals of time, more information becomes available if more detailed observations in time for each individual are made (cf. Arbous and Kerrich, 1951).

In another example of this kind recently discussed by Bailey (1953), households were classified according to the type of measles infection chain observed within the household. For a household of definite size (three and four were considered separately) the frequency distribution of the various possible types is calculable, being in fact for size 3:

Type of chain	Probability
1 case, 0 further cases	q^2
1 case, 1 further case.	$2\,pq^2$
1 case, 2 ' simultaneous ' further cases	p^2
1 case, leading to 1 case, which in turn leads to 1 case . .	$2\,p^2q$
	$\overline{1}$

(In this scheme p represents the probability of transmission of infection to one susceptible from one infection, and $q \equiv 1 - p$.) In the data examined by Bailey, the classical χ^2 theory had indicated that this simple theory was inadequate. However, if the probability of transmission was allowed to vary from household to household a satisfactory fit was obtained. The earlier heterogeneity example referred to warns us to be cautious of accepting this modification, while a reasonable one, as necessarily the right one on this evidence alone, but the agreement in the fitted constants between households of sizes 3 and 4 was a further point in its favour.

In this last example it will be noticed that the independence of the observations analysed, which relate to different households, is a reasonable assumption, but this may be far from true in other situations. Thus in a stochastic process which I call an 'immigration-emigration' process and to be referred to later, counts are made of individuals or particles in a certain area or volume. The marginal frequency distribution of these counts is Poissonian, but we must not test the goodness of fit of observed counts in an observed series by the standard χ^2 test, for the successive observations are correlated. This particular process is in fact what is called a Markov process, for which it has been shown by Patankar (1953) that

$$E(\chi^2) \sim k - 1 + 2 \sum_{1}^{\infty} \frac{\rho_1{}^s}{1 - \rho_1{}^s}$$

$$\sigma^2(\chi^2) \sim 2(k-1) + 8 \sum_{1}^{\infty} \frac{\rho_1{}^s}{(1 - \rho_1{}^s)^2} \, ,$$

where k is the number of classes and ρ_1 the first serial correlation. These formulae enable us to modify the standard χ^2 test to give an approximately valid test. Thus an observed distribution of the number of colloidal particles in a certain volume by Westgren (quoted by Chandrasekhar, 1943) was :

	0	1	2	3	4	5	6 or more	Total
Observed	381	568	357	175	67	28	7	1,583
Expected	379.6	542.0	387.0	184.2	65.8	18.8	5.6	1,583.0

The calculated value of χ^2 is 8.95 (for a theoretical mean value for the Poisson distribution of 1.428). The average value ($\rho_1 = 0.606$) is approximately 11.63, so the fit is obviously satisfactory; the theoretical variance of χ^2 is approximately 56.8.

Of course in such a case the relation between the successive observations will also be one of the major points of interest, and here we have a typical case no longer analysable by classical methods, that of a single series of *dependent* observations. Such dependence must also be recorded and tested. This may seem obvious enough when explicitly stated, but has often been neglected. For example, in plant ecology it is common to make 'quadrat counts' of some species over an area. Owing to heterogeneity or clumping of the plants, the frequency distribution of counts is often found to be not Poissonian, but more like a negative binomial distribution. A χ^2 test of such a modified distribution would again be invalid if the quadrat counts were systematically made over the area.

6

If, as has often been the case in practice, the quadrats were thrown at random, the classical test would approach validity as the area became large, but even so such a procedure is incapable of distinguishing many different stochastic (spatial) models or 'processes' which would lead to the same over-all frequency distribution of quadrat counts. Systematic counts over a grid of quadrats provide in principle more valuable data, but then raise the problem of how they are to be analysed. The problem is further complicated in this example because the underlying spatial process involves a variable (the presence of a plant, assumed of negligible area) which has almost always the value 0. The analysis of such processes, called 'point processes', has in the above context been discussed by Thompson (1955a, b).

It is possible to encounter examples of processes for which the dependence, while present, is not necessarily an obstacle to the use of quasi-classical methods. For example, probability chains of the type referred to a little earlier as models for measles cases within a household (starting, say, from one case) may yield large enough numbers to be considered in more detail for a single unit, say a school of 100 susceptibles (excluding the initial case). A chain of this kind might be ([1]):

Zero-th generation	1st generation	2nd	3rd	4th	5th
1	2	12	46	38	2

Such observed chains have been analysed by Helen Abbey (1952), a χ^2 test of goodness of fit of the number of cases at each stage making use of the number of susceptibles *observed* to remain from the previous stage for the purpose of calculating the 'expected' number of cases. Some precautions. are needed in analyses of this kind if biases are to be avoided. Thus in this example, if no cases had followed the initial case, no epidemic would have been available for analysis at all. However, for a large number n of susceptibles and certain conditions on the value of p, the probability of infection from case to susceptible, it has been shown by Joyce Almond (*loc. cit.*) that the χ^2 theory as used by Abbey is justifiable. Roughly speaking, for a restricted number of stages, and n large ([2]), the differences between the expected and observed numbers in previous stages have a negligible effect on the χ^2 term calculated at any particular stage from the new stochastic fluctuation that has occurred.

Returning, however, to the more straightforward type of

([1]) Quoted from Almond (1954).
([2]) It is this initial condition which provides here the necessary 'replication' for the statistical analysis to be possible.

sequence in one time dimension, for which we assumed we have a finite number of observations, let us consider the inference problem involved. While I have noted that no essentially new principle arises, it is clear that various extensions in theory are needed. Although much of the classical distribution theory for finite samples is exact, asymptotic theory, both in the properties of maximum likelihood estimates and in the χ^2 goodness of fit theory, still plays a dominant role. Thus, while some exact sampling theory is available for special stochastic process problems, it may be anticipated that asymptotic theory will be our first consideration here also.

The standard asymptotic theory of maximum likelihood estimates does not necessarily apply to dependent observations, and has to be re-considered. Any extensions will involve the generalization of the Central Limit Theorem to dependent observations. Such extensions are needed also for the asymptotic properties of L and its derivatives, where $L \equiv \log p$ is the logarithm of the probability of the sample (or of its probability density for continuous variables), and hence for goodness of fit theory. (The χ^2 expression introduced by Karl Pearson for measuring discrepancies between observed and theoretical frequencies is in the classical case asymptotically equivalent to formulae depending on L, but of course the log likelihood for stochastic processes may be of quite different character and give rise to different goodness of fit criteria.)

I will refer to one or two examples of some practical importance, to illustrate the kind of estimation theory that may arise. It will, however, be provisionally assumed that the asymptotic maximum likelihood theory may be validly applied; some further remarks on this point will be made in my concluding paragraphs.

2. ESTIMATION PROBLEM FOR SEQUENCES

(i) As a simple first example involving estimation, consider a sequences $X_0 \therefore X_n$ satisfying the linear autoregressive relation

$$X_r = \beta X_{r-1} + Y_r, \tag{1}$$

where the Y_r are independent normal variables with zero mean and variance σ_Y^2. The log likelihood function is then

$$L = -\frac{n+1}{2} \log(2\pi) - \frac{1}{2} \log \sigma^2(X_0) - \frac{n}{2} \log \sigma_Y^2$$

$$-\frac{1}{2} \times \frac{X_0^2}{\sigma^2(X_0)} - \frac{1}{2} \sum_{r=1}^{n} \frac{Y_r^2}{\sigma_Y^2}$$

where Y_r is given in terms of the X_r by (1). As n increases,

$$\frac{L}{n} = -\frac{1}{2}\log(2\pi) - \frac{1}{2}\log \sigma_Y^2 - \frac{1}{2n}\sum_{r=1}^{n}\frac{Y_r^2}{\sigma_Y^2} + 0\left(\frac{1}{n}\right),$$

and

$$\frac{\partial L}{\partial \beta} \sim \sum_{r=1}^{n}\frac{(X_r - \beta X_{r-1})\,X_{r-1}}{\sigma_Y^2}, \qquad (2)$$

whence the estimate of β is

$$\widehat{\beta} \sim \sum_{r=1}^{n} X_r X_{r-1} \Big/ \sum_{r=1}^{n} X_{r-1}^2. \qquad (3)$$

R. A. Fisher's information function for β gives

$$I(\beta) \equiv E\left(-\frac{\partial^2 L}{\partial\beta^2}\right) \sim E\left(\sum_{r=1}^{n}\frac{X_{r-1}^2}{\sigma_Y^2}\right)$$
$$= \frac{1}{\beta^2 - 1}\left[\frac{\beta^{2n} - 1}{\beta^2 - 1} - n\right] + \frac{\sigma^2(X_0)}{\sigma_Y^2}\left[-\frac{\beta^{2n} - 1}{\beta^2 - 1}\right]. \qquad (4)$$

The results (3) and (4) are general, and do not depend on any stationarity assumption for the sequence (1). However, we cannot expect to obtain much reliability for our *statistical* inferences unless some stability or homogeneity, providing in effect statistical replication, is present ([3]). This is automatically ensured in the classical case of a random sample of independent observations from the *same* population, and the analogue that suggests itself above is that of stationarity ([4]), the condition for which is $|\beta| < 1$. In this case (4) becomes

$$I(\beta) \sim \frac{n}{1 - \beta^2}. \qquad (5)$$

It is sometimes useful to obtain asymptotic interval estimates in problems of the above type. This may be done

---

([3]) I have elsewhere (1952) discussed the testing of a heterogeneous collection of realised events, but the probabilities for such events (and of all the unrealised contingencies, if more than simple dichotomies are involved) must first be assumed exactly known.

([4]) More strictly, that of ergodicity, which is, however, usually ensured by the stationarity condition.

directly in terms of the expression $\dfrac{\partial L}{\partial \beta}$, given in (2) for the present problem. Thus under the stationarity assumption the expression in (5) is also the variance of $\dfrac{\partial L}{\partial \beta}$, whose mean is zero. Its skewness I have shown to be (*Biometrika*, 1953)

$$E \left\{\left(\frac{\partial L}{\partial \beta}\right)^{3}\right\} = 2 E\left(\frac{\partial^{3} L}{\partial \beta^{3}}\right) + 3 \frac{\partial I(\beta)}{\partial \beta} = \frac{6\,n\beta}{(1-\beta^{2})^{2}} \cdot \quad (6)$$

The quantity σ_Y^2 has so far been assumed known. If it is unknown, it must also be estimated from the equation

$$\frac{\partial L}{\partial \alpha} \sim \frac{n}{2\,\alpha^{2}}\left(\sum_{r=1}^{n} \frac{(X_r - \beta X_{r-1})^{2}}{n} - \alpha\right), \quad (7)$$

where $\alpha \equiv \sigma_Y^2$, whence the estimate of α (for β assumed known) is

$$\widehat{\alpha}(\beta) = \sum_{r=1}^{n} \frac{(X_r - \beta X_{r-1})^{2}}{n} \cdot \quad (8)$$

The substitution of this estimate does not affect the interval estimated for β up to (and including) a relative accuracy $0\left(\dfrac{1}{\sqrt{n}}\right)$, the interval obtained on the basis of the asymptotic normality of $\dfrac{\partial L}{\partial \beta}$ and the above results being ([5])

$$\beta = \widehat{\beta} \pm \frac{\lambda}{\sqrt{n}} \Big/ (1 - \widehat{\beta^{2}}) + \frac{\widehat{\beta}}{n} + 0\left(\frac{1}{n^{3/2}}\right), \quad (9)$$

where λ is the usual normal law significance level (e.g. $\lambda = 1.96$ for a confidence probability of 0.95).

(ii) As a second example let us consider the immigration-emigration process referred to earlier. To obtain a simple (and only approximate) model of the number of particles or individuals in a small element of volume we assume that:

(a) the probability that any particle inside the volume at t is outside at time $t + dt$ is μdt, independently of other particles;

([5]) See Bartlett (1955b), where the estimate in (8) above is used in place of an incorrect one given in my previous Biometrika paper. This forthcoming paper also gives the modification to (9) if the mean of X is not zero and has also to be estimated.

(b) the probability that a particle enters the volume from outside during the interval dt is νdt.

Then by standard techniques (see, for example, Bartlett, 1955a) it may be shown that this process, which is Markovian, settles down to a stationary process for which the probability distribution for the numbers of particles inside the volume at two instants has the joint probability-generating function

$$\pi(z, w) = \exp \} m(z-1) + m(w-1)$$
$$+ me^{-\mu t}(z-1)(w-1)\{ \qquad (10)$$

where the mean number $m = \dfrac{\nu}{\mu}$.

There are two unknown parameters, which may be taken to be the mean m and $\rho = e^{-\mu\tau}$, where τ is the (known) time interval between successive observations. The exact maximum likelihood equations for m and ρ have been investigated by Patankar (cf. Bartlett, 1955a), but are complicated owing to the rather complicated mathematical expression for the conditional probability distribution of the number N_r, given the number N_{r-1} at the previous observed instant. However, the estimate for m comes out, not unnaturally, as the sample mean, and simpler asymptotic estimates for ρ when m is large may be investigated by noting that the joint distribution of N_r and N_{r-1} becomes normal as m increases. As n increases the estimate of ρ may be shown to be, in an iterative equation form,

$$\widehat{\rho} = \frac{C - 2(C - \widehat{\rho}V)/(1 - \widehat{\rho}^2)}{\widehat{m}} , \qquad (11)$$

where C is the sample autocovariance (for lag τ) and V the sample variance. It might be noticed that $\widehat{\rho}$ is not just $\dfrac{C}{V}$, as in the first example, because for a Poisson distribution the further information is available that the variance is equal to m. The asymptotic likelihood theory (the validity of which is for the moment being assumed) leads further to the results

$$\sigma^2(\widehat{m}) \sim \frac{m}{n} \frac{1+\rho}{1-\rho} , \qquad (12)$$

and

$$\sigma^2(\widehat{\rho}) \sim \frac{(1-\rho^2)^2}{(1+\rho^2)n} , \qquad (13)$$

(The estimates $\hat{m}$ and $\hat{\rho}$ have the further advantage that they are still obviously consistent estimates for finite m. Result (12) is easily shown to be valid for any m, but (13) is only valid for large m.)

The above process has been made use of by Rothschild (1953) as a model to estimate sperm speeds from consecutive cinemicrograph counts. He made use of the alternative and somewhat simpler estimate of ρ,

$$\check{\rho} = \frac{1}{\hat{m}}\left(1 - \frac{1}{2}\sum_{1}^{n}\frac{(X_r - X_{r-1})^2}{n}\right), \qquad (14)$$

which is also efficient for ρ near unity.

It has been noted that the above model is in this application, as in the application to suspensions of colloidal particles, somewhat oversimplified, so that it may be required to test its adequacy. In principle this may be carried out in detail on the observed frequencies of individual types of transition, by the methods I have developed for probability chains (Bartlett, 1950b) but unless extensive data are available the correlation technique for analysing stationary sequences in general is more convenient ([6]).

3. CORRELATION ANALYSIS OF STATIONARY SEQUENCES

When I last visited Brussels (in 1951) I made an attempt to survey briefly the inference problem for stationary time-series. It is not of course possible to do this, within a single lecture, in any detail, and I am not going to try to do so now. Perhaps the most useful thing I can do is to make a few remarks on this important problem, firstly, in relation to the even more general inference problem considered in this lecture, and secondly, on some of the more recent developments which have occurred since I was here last.

It is evident that our inference problem would be half solved, at least for a stationary sequence, if the specification were known sufficiently for the likelihood function to be written down apart from a few unknown parameters. Unfortunately, this is much more rarely possible than in the case of classical samples, for the *simultaneous* distribution of the n observations is now required; thus recourse to more general

---

([6]) For further discussion of methods of estimating mean speeds from counts, see Lindley (1954), Patil (1954), Rothschild and Ruben (1954).

methods is often necessary. The methods used for time-series may be compared with classical least squares and analysis of variance methods, and (as the series are assumed stationary) are expressible in terms of the correlation structure of the series. The main points to notice about such correlation analysis are as follows.

(i)   The simultaneous distribution of a *normal* stationary sequence depends (apart from the constant mean and variance) *only* on the autocorrelation function.

(ii)   A stationary series X_r occurring in practice may always be split up into two parts

$$X_r = Y_r + Z_r ,$$

where Y_r is a 'classical' component of harmonic terms, and Z_r is of autoregressive type. Z_r, which has a continuous 'spectrum', is moreover expressible as an autoregressive sum of the type

$$Z_r = \sum_{u=1}^{\infty} b_u Z_{r-u} + W_r ,$$

where the quantities W_r are *uncorrelated*.   In practice it is sometimes known, and more often plausible to assume, that in this expansion b_u is zero for $u > k$, say, and also that the W_r are completely *independent* of each other.   If this last assumption is true, the asymptotic fluctuation theory of sample correlations from normal sequences holds also for (single) autoregressive series of the type Z_r.

(iii)   Classical periodogram analysis applies to series of the type Y_r, or at most $Y_r + W_r$; it was the breakdown of such methods for series of the type Z_r that led statisticians, following Yule (1927), to study autoregressive or autocorrelation methods of analysis.   However, there is a well-known Fourier relation between the true autocorrelation function and the true spectral function or spectrum of the series, and an analogous linear relation between the corresponding sample functions.   This suggests that which of these two approaches is used may be to some extent a matter of convenience, at least if harmonic or periodogram analysis is properly used.   Work in recent years, for example by Whittle (1951, 1952*a*, *b*, 1954), Grenander (1951), Grenander and Rosenblatt (1952, 1954) and myself (1950*c*, 1954) has been in particular concerned with such extensions to the periodogram approach ([7]).

([7]) For a recent discussion in some detail of this approach see the second paper of mine referred to.

Whittle's work has largely been based on the likelihood function for normal processes, and a formulation of this function in terms of the theoretical spectrum (this being of course possible owing to the theoretical equivalence of the spectral and correlation functions). One problem he has discussed (1952b) is that of disentangling the components Y_r and Z_r for a process with *both* components present, though this difficult problem still requires further investigation before practical recommendations on its solution can be considered finalised. A summary (1954) of Whittle's work has been given by him as an Appendix to the new edition of Wold's *Stationary Time Series*.

The other work referred to has been concerned with methods of estimating the continuous spectrum of a time-series of type Z_r. In the more recent of this work, initiated by Grenander and Rosenblatt, methods of constructing entire confidence bands for spectra of this type have been discussed. In my own most recent (1954) paper on spectral analysis I have suggested what I believe to be improvements on Grenander and Rosenblatt's proposals.

Methods of analysing multiple series have been discussed by myself and Rajalakshman (1953) and Whittle (1953), making theoretical use respectively of correlational and spectral formulations. In the paper (1954) by Miss Patil already referred to, this multiple series technique has been used to demonstrate the failure of the immigration-emigration process in its simplest Markovian form when applied to sperm counts, this being more readily detectable in the extension to more than one region under observation.

4. PROCESSES SPECIFIED FOR CONTINUOUS TIME

When we consider continuous time-records, it is quite obvious that theoretical extensions are required, for some equivalent of the likelihood functions has to be set up. In practice we know that a finite set of coordinates must suffice to describe observed data, and correspondingly we assume that a record of finite duration can be described by a co-ordinate sequence which is finite or at least enumerable. Two of the most useful procedures are:

(1) for (mean spare) continuous processes, we consider the values at n consecutive points t_1, ..., t_n, and then let n increase such that $\max(t_r - t_{r-1})$ decreases to zero;

(2) for processes $X(t)$ for which $dX(t)$ is zero except at an enumerable number of random times T_1, ..., T_N (N is also random with $P\{N < \infty\} = 1$), the probability may be specified

in terms of these times and the corresponding values of $dX(t)$, together with $X(0)$ and N.

In the paper referred to at the beginning of this lecture, Grenander (1950) has considered more general representations. The essential point is that the *likelihood ratio*, which in classical theory appears in the theory of statistical tests but not usually in estimation theory, is the quantity which is still definable in general. If the likelihood ratio is evaluated for a variable hypothesis H against a fixed hypothesis H_0, say, it can be precisely used in estimation problems also, and exact or 'small-sample' estimation theory is in principle available as well as asymptotic theory.

I am, however, somewhat doubtful that situations will present themselves very often for which more than asymptotic theory will be possible. The difficulties may conveniently be illustrated on an example discussed by Grenander (but only in regard to the estimation of the mean m) viz. the continuous analogue of the first process considered in § 2 (cf. also Bartlett, 1950a). We write

$$dX(t) + \mu X(t) dt = dZ(t) , \qquad (15)$$

where $Z(t)$ is a normal additive process. To include Grenander's derivation for the estimate of m, we set up first the likelihood of n observations X_r at intervals Δt from the process (15), with a non-zero mean m included, i.e.

$$X_r - m = \beta (X_{r-1} - m) + Y_r , \qquad (16)$$

with $\beta \equiv e^{-\mu \Delta t}$. Then if L is the log likelihood of these observations, we readily find as $\Delta t \to 0$ but $n\Delta t = T$

$$\lim \{ L(m, \mu, \sigma^2) - L(0, 1, \sigma^2) \}$$
$$= \frac{-\mu [X(0) - m]^2}{\sigma^2} + \frac{X^2(0)}{\sigma^2}$$
$$+ \frac{1}{2 \sigma^2} \left(-2\mu \int_0^T [X(t) - m] dX(t) - \mu^2 \int_0^T [X(t) - m]^2 dt \right)$$
$$+ \frac{1}{2 \sigma^2} \left(2 \int_0^T X(t) dX(t) + \int_0^T X^2(t) dt \right) + \frac{1}{2} \log \mu . \qquad (17)$$

It will be noticed that the log of a likelihood ratio with fixed hypothesis $H_0 \equiv (m = 0, \mu = 1, \sigma^2 = \sigma^2)$ has been taken, where σ^2 is the unknown variance increment of $Z(t)$ per unit time. The estimation of σ^2 has thus been temporarily deferred, for reasons I will give later. The precise estimation of m and μ are thus given by the equations [where L now for convenience denotes the limiting expression given in (17)]

$$\frac{\partial L}{\partial m} = \frac{\mu (2 + \mu T)}{\sigma^2} \left(\frac{X(0) + X(T) + \mu \int_0^T X(t)\, dt}{2 + \mu T} - m \right), \quad (18)$$

$$\frac{\partial L}{\partial \mu} = \frac{1}{2\mu} - \frac{[X(0) - m]^2}{\sigma^2}$$

$$- \frac{\int_0^T [X(t) - m]\, dX(t)}{\sigma^2} - \frac{\mu \int_0^T [X(t) - m]^2\, dt}{\sigma^2}. \quad (19)$$

From the mathematical form of (18), we obtain Grenander's interesting result that if μ is known then the optimum unbiased estimate of m is

$$\widehat{m} = \frac{X(0) + X(T) + \mu \int_0^T X(t)\, dt}{2 + \mu T}, \quad (20)$$

with variance

$$\sigma^2(\widehat{m}) = \frac{\sigma^2}{\mu(2 + \mu T)}. \quad (21)$$

This result, unlike the asymptotic least-squares theory

$$\widehat{m} \sim \frac{\int_0^T X(t)\, dt}{T} \quad (22)$$

with variance

$$\sigma^2(\widehat{m}) \sim \frac{\sigma^2}{\mu^2 T}, \quad (23)$$

is exact; however, if μ is not known, an estimate must be substituted from (19), and as the *two* equations are note of the optimum form, no advantage over the asymptotic theory is necessarily gained. The precise estimate $\widehat{\mu}$ from (19) moreover requires a knowledge of σ^2, though for large T we may, as in the discrete time case, neglect the first two terms, obtaining the asymptotic estimate

$$\mu \sim \frac{- \int_0^T [X(t) - m]\, dX(t)}{\int_0^T [X(t) - m]^2\, dt}. \quad (24)$$

This 'least-squares' estimate has asymptotic variance $\dfrac{2\,\mu}{T}$ (a least squares estimate may conveniently be defined as any estimate equivalent to the maximum likelihood estimate, apart from possible end-correction effects, on the assumption that the process is normal).

The reason for not including the estimation of σ^2 is that the above formulation is not strictly realistic as $\Delta t \to 0$. In the estimation equation for σ^2 we should obtain a term

$$\lim_{\Delta t \to 0} \frac{\Sigma(\Delta X)^2}{T},$$

which (as ΔX is of order $\sqrt{\Delta T}$) exists, but could not be evaluated in practice. The difficulty is due to the assumption of a *normal* process, which provides in principle an infinite number of degrees of freedom for estimating σ^2, and would not arise if the disturbances ΔZ were of more general additive type. However, if we alternatively assumed that they were purely *discontinuous* in character, they would not give rise to more than a finite number of discontinuities in the interval T, and the parameter μ could be measured exactly from the observed decay in $X(t)$ between such jumps. The model is in fact likely to be over-idealized, and the estimates with apparently infinite accuracy to which it leads are probably less satisfactory than estimates less dependent on the precise form of the likelihood function.

Genuine processes of the purely discontinuous type do of course occur when the variable is an integer, and may lead to formulations of the second type mentioned at the beginning of this section. Suppose, for example, an immigration-emigration process had been observed continuously, so that the times at which the number $N(t)$ increased or decreased by one were known. The likelihood of observations over a pre-determined interval T is rather more complicated than that for a predetermined number of transitions, for the probabilities of the successive observations cannot be evaluated in sequence in the former case. However, if such a record of arbitrary length were available, it could be considered for a given number of transitions, and the probabilities (or probability densities) of the initial number, the lengths of the intervals between jumps and of the jumps being up or down by one, would be multiplied consecutively to obtain the likelihood function in terms of the parameters μ and ν. For example, for a record beginning

$$N(0)=3, \quad dN(2)=+1, \quad dN(3)=-1,$$

the likelihood function so far would be

$$\frac{\left(\frac{\nu}{\mu}\right)^3 e^{-\nu/\mu}}{3\,!} \cdot (3\,\mu + \nu)\, e^{-(3\mu+\nu)2} \cdot \frac{\nu}{3\,\mu + \nu}$$

$$\cdot (4\,\mu + \nu)\, e^{-(4\mu+\nu)} \cdot \frac{4\,\mu}{4\,\mu + \nu} \ .$$

For such a likelihood, the probability densities from the time intervals provide information on μ, say, when $\frac{\mu}{\nu}$ is assumed known, and the jumps [with $N(0)$ if used] provide information on $\frac{\mu}{\nu}$.

Discussion of the estimation of the parameters λ and μ of a simple birth-and-death process has been given by D. G. Kendall (1952) and Moran (1951). The likelihood for such a process is simpler in that the transitions up or down depend on coefficients $N\lambda$ and $N\mu$, so that the lengths of the time intervals are always proportional to the same sum $(\lambda + \mu)$, and the jumps on the same probability $\frac{\lambda}{\lambda + \mu}$; the circumstance that when $N = 0$ the process terminates must, however, be borne in mind. I have preferred to refer to the immigration-emigration process here because, in spite of the theoretical importance of the birth-and-death process, it is more difficult to envisage it arising in practice (at least in such a simplified form). It might also be noticed that as the birth-and-death process, in contrast with the immigration-emigration process, is not stationary, effective replication is only obtained if $N(0)$ is large (cf. the epidemic chain referred to towards the end of § 1).

5. FURTHER THEORETICAL PROBLEMS

It has been suggested that in the lectures for this Collo-quium a reference to specific problems still awaiting solution would be of interest. In the general inference problem I have been discussing, the results so far reached are promising and useful, but they are little more than initial stages in the exploration of a comparatively new territory. Ideally, small-sample results similar to those now available in many 'classical' inference problems are needed, though I have suggested that asymptotic results are, at least to start with, much more feasible.

However, it should be possible to study the rapidity with which the asymptotic results become valid as the sample increases in size. For example, in time-series analysis there is some evidence that Quenouille's goodness of fit test for auto-regressive series tends to exaggerate significance (cf. Rao and Som, 1951, Bartlett and Rajalakshman, 1953), and correction for this may be needed. The various asymptotic tests on the periodogram may vary enormously in their validity for samples of finite length (Bartlett, 1954), and further investigation of this is essential. The comparative merits of different smoothing procedures on the periodogram, in spite of some further investigations by J. Medhi and myself (1955), still perhaps need final assessment. The procedure suggested by Whittle (1952b) for disentangling the discrete and continuous spectral components for a time-series with mixed spectrum is, as I mentioned earlier, provisional in character.

Another aspect of this asymptotic validity is that criteria obtained from a likelihood specification are sometimes more difficult to handle than other criteria asymptotically equivalent. As an example the Quenouille test is simpler to apply than the likelihood criterion, but while their asymptotic equivalence under certain conditions has been noted (Walker, 1952), the extent of their divergence for finite samples requires further elucidation.

One essential point in the asymptotic theory (referred to in § 1) has so far in this lecture been deferred, and that is the validity of the classical asymptotic likelihood theory in the domain of time-series or other stochastic processes. Again, this is partly because such extensions still remain to be investigated, especially for stochastic processes specified in continuous time (cf., however, Grenander, 1951). In the case of stationary time-series in discrete time, various paper are now beginning to provide the required theoretical results (Mann and Wald, 1943; Diananda, 1953, 1954; Walker, 1954). Even in the relatively simple case of finite probability chains (Bartlett, 1950b), the extension to the immigration-emigration process has not strictly been covered ([8]). In general, by analogy with the probability chains case, we should expect classical asymptotic properties to apply in the case of completely stationary and ergodic processes, with perhaps some further condition on the rapidity with which the dependence between neighbouring observations drops off. (In the discussion on my survey of time-series analysis given at the London 1950 conference on Information Theory, Professor Moran made the

([8]) The enumerable case has recently been treated by C. Derman (to be published).

interesting suggestion that Central Limit Theorem extensions in the case of time-series might be classifiable in terms of the information (entropy) measure of the series, but I am not aware of any follow-up of this suggestion.)

So much for purely theoretical problems. I am myself conscious of a vaguer but fundamental practical problem which is emerging in the statistical analysis of stochastic process. It can be exemplified in the field of epidemiology. Here I have referred to one or two specific inference problems, but there is the wider inference problem of, say, comparing notifications of some infectious disease for a whole area with some theoretical model. The difficulties are at present insurmountable. In the first place, the theoretical consequences of even grossly over-simplified models are not yet possible to evaluate mathematically; even if they were, the over-simplification implies that a perfect fit with observation would not be expected. Nevertheless, not only should we like some yardstick of agreement in order to compare different models, but certain observed phenomena cannot be assessed without some appropriate model as a theoretical specification. For example, measles notifications show a seasonal variation, but bearing in mind a tendency to a two-year epidemic cycle and dependence between epidemics in different places, how should we assess the significance of an observed apparent divergence from the long-term seasonal variation? It seems likely here that statistical inference in the precise sense will remain associated with local or isolated data, such as households or schools, and with the aid of such results available agreement between observation and theory over wider domains would be assessed in a more qualitative manner. This seems quite consistent with scientific method in general. After all, in some fields, such as the theory of evolution, actual measurements are necessarily confined to local or temporary situations or experiments, such as investigating mutation rates, local competition and survival, etc. The statistical analysis of stochastic processes is in any case likely to show a considerable range of approach owing to its close interrelation with the theoretical specification or model, an appropriate choice for which becomes of far greater importance in the inference problem for stochastic processes, if only because (as I noted in my opening remarks) the choice is *a priori* so much wider.

References

ABBEY, H. (1952), *An examination of the Reed-Frost theory of epidemics* (*Human Biology*, **3**, 201).

ALMOND, J. (1954), *A note on the χ^2 test applied to epidemic chains* (*Biometrics*, **10**, 459).

ARBOUS, A. G. and KERRICH, J. E. (1951), *Accident statistics and the concept of accident proneness* (*Biometrics*, **7**, 340).

ARMITAGE, P. (1951), *The statistical theory of bacterial populations subject to mutation* (*J. Roy. Statist. Soc.*, **B**, **14**, 1).

BAILEY, N. T. J. (1953), *The use of chain binomials with a variable chance of infection for the analysis of intra-household epidemics* (*Biometrika*, **40**, 279).

BARTLETT, M. S. (1950a), *The statistical approach to the analysis of time series* (*Symposium on Information Theory* [mimeographed Proceedings, Ministry of Supply, London]).

— (1950b), *The frequency goodness of fit test for probability chains* (*Proc. Camb. Phil. Soc.*, **47**, 86).

— (1950c), *Periodogram analysis and continuous spectra* (*Biometrika*, **37**, 1).

— (1952), *The statistical significance of odd bits of information* (*Biometrika*, **39**, 228).

— (1953), *Approximate confidence intervals* (*Biometrika*, **40**, 12 and 306).

— (1954), *Problèmes de l'analyse spectrale des séries temporelles stationnaires* (*Publ. Inst. Stat.*, *Univ. de Paris*, **3**, fasc 3, 119).

— (1955a), *An Introduction to Stochastic Processes* (Cambridge, in Press).

— (1955b), *Approximate confidence intervals. III. A bias correction* (*Biometrika*, **42**, 201).

BARTLETT, M. S. and MEDHI, J. (1955), *On the efficiency of procedures for smoothing periodograms from time series with continuous spectra* (*Biometrika*, **42**, 143).

BARTLETT, M. S. and RAJALAKSHMAN, D. V. (1953), *Goodness of fit tests for simultaneous autoregressive series* (*J. Roy. Statist. Soc.*, **B 15**, 107).

CHANDRASEKHAR, S. (1943), *Stochastic problems in physics and astronomy* (*Rev. Mod. Phys.*, **15**, 1).

DIANANDA, P. H. (1953), *Some probability limit theorems with statistical applications* (*Proc. Camb. Phil. Soc.*, **49**, 239).

— (1954), *The central limit theorem for m-dependent variables asymptotically stationary to second order* (*Proc. Camb. Phil. Soc.*, **50**, 287).

GRENANDER, U. (1950), *Stochastic processes and statistical inference* (*Ark. Mat.*, **1**, 195).

— (1951), *On empirical spectral analysis of stochastic processes* (*Ark. Mat.*, **1**, 503).

GRENANDER, U. and ROSENBLATT, M. (1952), *On spectral analysis of stationary time-series* (*Proc. Nat. Acad. Sci. Wash.*, **38**, 519).

— (1954), *Statistical spectral analysis of time-series arising from stationary stochastic processes* (*Ann. Math. Statist.*, **24**, 537).

KENDALL, D. G. (1952), *Les processus stochastiques de croissance en biologie* (*Ann. Inst. Poincaré*, **13**, fasc. 1, 43).

LINDLEY, D. V. (1954), *The estimation of velocity distributions from counts* (*Amsterdam Mathematical Conference*).

MORAN, P. (1951), *Estimation methods for evolutive processes* (*J. Roy. Statist. Soc.*, **B 13**, 141).

OF STOCHASTIC PROCESSES 89

MANN, H. B and WALD, A. (1943), *On the statistical treatment of linear stochastic difference equations* (*Econometrica*, **11**, 173).

PATANKAR, V. N. (1953), *The goodness of fit of frequency distributions obtained from stochastic processes*, Ph. D. Thesis, University of Manchester.

PATIL, V. T. (1954), *The consistency and adequacy of the Poisson Markoff model for density Fluctuations* (submitted to *Biometrika*).

RAO, S. R. and SOM, R. K. (1951), *The applicability of large sample tests for moving average and autoregressive schemes to series of short length—an experimental study.* Part 2: *Autoregressive series* (*Sankhya*, **11**, 239).

ROTHSCHILD, Lord (1953), *A new method of measuring the activity of spermatozoa* (*J. Exp. Biol.*, **30**, 178).

ROTHSCHILD, Lord and RUBEN, H. (1954), *Estimation of mean speeds of organisms and particles by counting* (to be published).

THOMPSON, H. R. (1955a), *Spatial point processes, with applications to ecology* (*Biometrika*, **42**, 102).

— (1955b), *The statistical study of plant distribution patterns using a grid of contiguous quadrats* (submitted to *Journal of Ecology*).

WALKER, A. M. (1952), *Some properties of the asymptotic power functions of goodness-of-fit tests for linear autoregressive schemes* (*J. Roy. Statist. Soc.*, **114**, 117).

— (1954), *The asymptotic distribution of serial correlation coefficients for autoregressive processes with dependent residuals* (*Proc. Cam. Phil. Soc.*, **50**, 60).

WHITTLE, P. (1951), *Hypothesis testing in time series analysis*, Upsala.

— (1952a), *Tests of fit in time series* (*Biometrika*, **39**, 309).

— (1952b), *The simultaneous estimation of a time series harmonic components and covariance structure* (*Trab. Estadistica*, **3**, 43).

— (1953), *The analysis of multiple stationary time series* (*J. Roy. Statist. Soc.*, **B 15**, 125).

— (1954), *Some recent contributions to the theory of stationary processes.* Appendix 2 to the second edition of *A Study in the Analysis of Stationary Time-Series*, by H. Wold, Upsala.

YULE, G. E. (1927), *On the method of investigating periodicities in disturbed series, with special reference to Wolfer's sun-spot numbers* (*Phil. Trans.*, **A 226**, 267).

7

Applications of Probability and Statistical Theory in Biology

Introductory remarks

First of all may I express my appreciation of the honour of being invited through your Academy of Sciences to address this Section; I would also like to speak for my colleagues in England in hoping for further exchanges of lecturers and visitors between our respective countries.

Coming now to my paper, this was stimulated by some specific ecological problems, and a more detailed discussion of these formed a major part of my first written draft.* However, in the time at my disposal I could not hope to present such details adequately, and I felt, at the risk of over-generality, that an introductory survey of the use of probability theory in biology might be worth while. For this, it is essential also to consider the closely related role of statistical investigations in biology. In spite of the negligible mathematical content of this shortened paper, I think that such an occasional survey is quite relevant at a Congress of the present kind, as it helps to give a proper perspective to more specific mathematical contributions in the important and general field under review.

1. *The statistical method*

Without attempting to decide on when and where the very first work either in probability or in statistical method arose, I will recall that at about the same time as Pascal and Fermat were beginning in France to crystallize probability theory into a valuable mathematical calculus, the empirical statistical method of investigation was being represented in England by

[* This part was subsequently published in *Biometrika*, **44** (1957), 27.]

the publications of Graunt (1662) and Halley (1693).† Thus if it is permitted to include such early actuarial observations within the general field of biology (and later studies of this nature by the Belgian statistician Quetelet, in the early nineteenth century, led directly on to the biological statistics of Galton), the use of statistics in biology preceded by at least two hundred years the development of statistical concepts in physics. However, this comparison is not altogether a fair one, for while I have in mind the growth of statistical mechanics in the second half of the nineteenth century, the statistical biology to which I have referred was still largely empirical and observational. Statistical *theories* in biology hardly began until nearer the time of statistical mechanics, with the work of Darwin. As Schrödinger (1949) has remarked, 'I dare say the first scientific man aware of the vital role of statistics was Charles Darwin. His theory hinges on the law of big numbers.' But even the theory of natural selection was hardly quantitative in character at this early stage, and quantitative statistical theory in biology, to which I shall return presently, is even more recent.

The development of statistical methods in biology was greatly stimulated by the friendship and collaboration among Galton, Weldon and Karl Pearson at the end of the last century. Their investigations were mainly confined to observational (in contrast with experimental) material; this circumstance helps to explain the importance they placed on the concept of correlation, due, in this biological context, to Galton (1888). The further great development of statistical methods in England in the present century is largely associated with the name of R. A. Fisher, and one of its important characteristics is its emphasis on valid and efficient statistical analyses of agricultural and other biological experiments, with repercussions on the proper design of such experiments. A somewhat distinct but related development is that of precise statistical assessments in bio-assay (see, for example, Finney, 1952).

† Cf. also the remarks on early Italian developments by C. Gini (discussion following Cochran, 1950, p. 82) and M. G. Kendall (1956).

2. *Theoretical analysis of statistical phenomena in biology*

In spite of the very great value of these statistical methods, it is perhaps not unfair to say that they should be classified as somewhat empirical in character. The introduction of precise statistical experimentation, especially when strict randomization procedures were used, enabled quantitative and unambiguous causal relations between treatments and results to be established. The importance of such statistical inferences is evident when we contrast them with the weaker ones which are all that are available when experimentation and randomization in this strict sense are not possible (a well-known recent example being the statistical, but not yet certainly causal, relation observed between cigarette smoking and lung cancer). However, in the absence of any further scientific theory underlying even well-established experimental causal relations, they do not justify much extrapolation from the particular experimental conditions tested. Moreover, if the observations on any single experimental 'unit' (which may be an individual or an entire group) are not simple, but themselves form a protracted and complex sequence, then the problem of their inter-relation for a single unit still remains.

Thus there is some justification for Kostitzin (1939), when considering the place of mathematics in biology, to claim (p. 17):

> Mathematics gained entry into Natural Science by the statistical door, but this stage passes to the stage of analysis as in all quantitative sciences. The function of the statistical method is to clear the ground, to establish a certain number of empirical laws, and so to facilitate the transition from statistics to analysis. The labour of doing this is considerable, and important, but when it is done the first duty passes to mathematical analysis, which, at this stage in the growth of a quantitative science, is alone able to trace out the causes of phenomena and to deduce from them all the logical consequences. At this stage even approximate hypotheses as to the true nature of the phenomena are often more useful than empirical laws. . . .

Such mathematics need not all be statistical in conception, though the importance of statistical theory for *populations* is to be expected, and, as already noted, was already implicitly recognized in Darwin's theory of evolution by natural selection. I should perhaps make it clear that by statistical theory I mean the application of the mathematical theory of probability to statistical aggregates, in the sense that has been admirably stated by Khintchine (1949, p. 1):

> This science has for its main task the study of group phenomena, that is, such phenomena as occur in collections of a large number of objects of essentially the same kind, . . . the discovery of such general laws as are implied by the gross character of the phenomena and depend comparatively little on the nature of the individual objects.

The stability of averages from large aggregates enabled many physical laws to be formulated at first in deterministic form, even although the underlying interpretation of these laws was statistical in character. The same trend may be discerned in biological mathematics, where most of the early discussion of the growth and fluctuations in populations, for example, in the realms of ecology or epidemiology, was made without reference to probability theory. A notable early exception was the discussion by Francis Galton (1889) of the 'extinction of surnames' problem raised by Alphonse de Candolle, a fundamental problem which is linked on the one hand with the gambler's ruin problem in classical probability theory and on the other with extinction phenomena in evolutionary, epidemiological and ecological theories.

It may legitimately be asked how much justification there is for applying probability theory to biological phenomena. Here there are in my view two relevant points to make:

Firstly, any fundamental philosophical attitude to determinism or indeterminism is immaterial to the bulk of statistical laws in physics or in biology. The justification of the probability calculus rests on the same sort of basis as in its original application to gambling, namely that even if a multiplicity of detailed causes is operating to produce the observed broad classes of events, it is an economy of thought in the sense of Mach to ignore these and appeal merely to the operations of chance and the laws of averages (cf. Schrödinger, 1944; and Gause, 1934, footnote on p. 124).

Secondly, it is true that a successful application of probability or statistical theory in one field does not necessarily imply its relevance in another. In biology the individuals may themselves be complex organisms, unlike the anonymous atoms of physics. Here the statistical approach can have more or less relevance, depending on its context and the nature of the application (as is well recognized, even for human populations, in the realm of insurance). Its relevance in terms of probability theory is greatest when the processes are dependent on 'accidental' happenings, such as the natural selection of a new gene arising by mutation, or infection from person to person by the transmission of an invisible virus; in such cases, the working hypothesis of 'blind chance', in the sense indicated above, is entirely reasonable.

3. *The study of specific stochastic processes*

It is obviously impossible to give more than the most cursory mention of the specific biological fields where statistical theory can be applied.‡ One well-known general field is that of genetics, and the statistical consequences of gene recombinations and gene mutations in relation to the theory of evolution have been the subject of extended study, for example, by R. A. Fisher, J. B. S. Haldane and Sewall Wright. From the standpoint of probability theory, such evolutionary changes in biological populations are classified under the general heading of stochastic processes, to the mathematical theory of which Russian probabilists (Markov, Kolmogorov, Khintchine, Slutsky and many others) have made such fundamental contributions. The systematic study of population genetics in terms of

‡ A somewhat heterogeneous but informative compendium of papers is to be found in the publication edited by Kempthorne, Bancroft, Gowen and Lush (1954).

stochastic process theory is comparatively recent (see Feller, 1951; Crow and Kimura, 1956).

A significant trend in statistical psychology is a tendency to break away from preoccupation with static correlational studies of ability to more dynamic studies of learning processes. While these latter studies make use of new stochastic models for learning (Bush and Mosteller, 1955; Cane, 1956), such models are at present formulated in semi-empirical terms. Eventually it may prove possible to link them up with independent studies of nervous and cerebral organization, studies in which the enormous numbers of nerve cells and fibres involved require a statistical viewpoint (McCulloch and Pitts, 1948; Walter, 1956). Among such statistical models of development and change within a single organism could perhaps also be included the work of Turing (1952), who showed how diffusion processes might play a vital role in the development of stationary morphological patterns.

A field of study in which I have myself been interested for some time is epidemiology, in connection with the theory of epidemics resulting from transmission of infection from person to person. A recent historical survey of this field has been given by Serfling (1952). As I have shown elsewhere (Bartlett, 1956), theoretical models indicate, among other things, the extent to which population *size* may sometimes be crucial for the probable sequence of events, and thus, for example, show to what extent laboratory observations on infected animal populations will have any similarity to larger-scale field observations *even if the same model applies to both*. One important stochastic problem that arises in the theory of recurrent epidemics is the chance of extinction of the infecting agent. In the case of the virus infection of measles there is a critical community size (of the order of 100,000 in my country) which can maintain recurrent epidemics: below this size, the maintenance of epidemics depends on infection from outside, as is well known for measles in the case of very small village or island communities.

The essential theoretical point here is the explicit recognition of the discrete character of populations and the stochastic or random aspect of changes, as distinct from strictly deterministic formulations. Epidemiological studies have often been referred to in ecological discussions, especially as they can logically be classified under the general heading of ecology. Thus the formulation of epidemic theory in probability terms, which goes back to the brilliant early but rather overlooked papers on stochastic processes by McKendrick (1914, 1926), has a natural counterpart in the study of population growth and change in animal ecology.

In this field the mathematical work of Lotka (1925), Volterra (1926) and subsequent writers on the growth and interaction of biological populations, while formulated in deterministic terms, constitutes a permanent contribution to the understanding of how such populations can behave. Differences of opinion are obviously possible on the *degree* to which admittedly over-simplified models can explain some of the complex observational phenomena to be found in nature. Criticisms from biologists, however, have been sometimes justified and sometimes unjustified, for any arguments that such models have no value, or alternatively no limitations, are equally pointless. A significant constructive survey was made by Gause (1934), when he attempted to bridge the gap between theoretical models and natural biological ecology. Biologists who are doubtful of the value either of theoretical models or of such experiments, as being both unrepresentative of nature, might consider the role of these approaches in the physical sciences.

The need for stochastic ecological models was perhaps already envisaged by Gause (1934, p. 124) but became quite apparent in the experiments by Park with the flour beetle *Tribolium*. Here one of two species kept together in a container did not survive every time, but had a definite survival probability (e.g. 30 per cent of times), that could be estimated by replication and changed by changing the environment (see, for example, Neyman, Park and Scott, 1956).

There is now no mathematical difficulty in the *formulation* of stochastic models (see, for example, Bartlett, 1955a, 1956), and such formulations have already been made for typical ecological models by Chin Long Chiang (see Kempthorne *et al.*, 1954). The greater intractability of even the simplest of these is, however, a serious obstacle to progress, especially in animal ecology, where even in the deterministic formulations of Lotka and Volterra many simplifications such as neglect of age-structure or of other heterogeneity were made.

One point that has been emphasized in my own detailed investigation is the enhanced value of deterministic formulations of population dynamics when properly interpreted within more comprehensive stochastic models. Cases I have considered are (1) the logistic model of population growth for a single species, (2) the classical Lotka–Volterra predator–prey relation, (3) competition between two species, with special reference to Park's investigations on the competition between the two species of flour-beetle, *Tribolium confusum* and *Tribolium castaneum*.

Perhaps before ending this rapid survey of biological applications I may return briefly to the problem of the statistical analysis of biological observations. When the latter represent realizations of stochastic processes, the standard techniques of statistics do not necessarily apply, and a careful consideration of the underlying stochastic mechanism is essential (Bartlett, 1955a, b). Sometimes, when deliberately over-simplified and provisional models are being used, no more than a very crude comparison with actual data may be justifiable.

4. *Associated mathematical problems*

The biological applications of probability and statistical theory to which I have briefly referred may conveniently be classified under the generic title of biometry. The relevance of the theory of stochastic processes to these applications emphasizes that there are many associated mathematical problems; but if, through bearing in mind the primarily mathematical character of this Congress, I had merely concentrated on these, it would have distorted the scientific picture I wished to convey. However, without wishing to go into the purely abstract aspects of stochastic process theory, I might recall here some of the approaches of use—for example, the formal but very general equation which I have used (see, for example, Bartlett, 1955) to depict and study the mathematical 'evolution' of a time-homogeneous Markovian stochastic process (in physics or in biology):

$$M_t = e^{Ht}M_0, \qquad (1)$$

where M_t is the characteristic function of the stochastic variables at time t, and H is some operator independent of t corresponding to an equation

$$\frac{\partial M_t}{\partial t} = HM_t \qquad (2)$$

for the rate of change of M_t. Equation (2), when available, is equivalent to Kolmogorov's general 'forward' equation for a Markov process, and in particular includes his diffusion equation, which indeed is often the best approximative equation when the exact equation (2) is intractable. (In this connection see, for example, the genetical examples in Crow and Kimura, 1956; although, as these authors point out, precautions are necessary with the diffusion approximation if there are absorbing or semi-absorbing boundaries, i.e. the extinction phenomenon is present.) In cases where an equilibrium distribution exists, it must obviously from (2) satisfy the equation

$$\frac{\partial M_t}{\partial t} = 0 = HM_t: \qquad (3)$$

this equation has in effect been used, in its diffusion approximative form, by Sewall Wright to obtain the equilibrium distribution in some genetical problems. It is, however, advisable to check that the solution M_∞ so found is in fact $\lim M_t$ as $t \to \infty$.

A further generalization of equation (1), necessary both in physics and biology, covers cases where a continuum of stochastic variables is involved, such as particles with a continuous range of energy or position, or individuals with a continuous range of age or position. Such processes have, following H. Wold, been termed 'point processes' (see, for example, Bartlett, 1954), and their rigorous specification may either be dealt with directly, or included in recent generalizations of stochastic 'distributions' (in the sense of Schwartz).

Simple 'multiplicative' processes, where each individual propagates independently of others, are more conveniently solved via an integral equation equivalent to Kolmogorov's 'backward' equation. In particular, extinction probabilities for such processes are obtained directly by this method, which leads also to recurrence equations for them in other more complicated processes.

The symbolic solution (1) suggests (analogously to the Schrödinger equation in quantum mechanics) the semi-group character of time-homogeneous Markov processes. A rigorous study of this semi-group aspect has recently been started by mathematical probabilists, for example, by W. Feller in America, and by D. G. Kendall and H. Reuter in England. This work, while at first sight rather abstract for practical applicability, nevertheless promises to assist in the difficult mathematical task of studying the properties of specific stochastic models in biology. Thus, in the problem of competition between species, extinction probabilities, of the kind discussed in the more detailed draft of this paper, are being considered by Kendall and Reuter with the aid of this general technique.

An alternative direct stochastic representation of a Markov model is familiar in simple *linear* diffusion equations, but I have recently made some use of this approach for more complicated non-linear equations. With this representation the relation of the stochastic equation to its deterministic approximation is more apparent; for if a deterministic population model is, say,

$$\frac{dn_t}{dt} = f(n_t), \qquad (4)$$

where n_t is the vector of population sizes for k different species, then the stochastic model might be written

$$dN_t = f(N_t)\, dt + dZ_t \tag{5}$$

where N_t is the corresponding stochastic population vector, and dZ_t has zero mean and known covariance matrix $G(N_t)\, dt$ (being a combination of Poisson variables, adjusted to have zero means). The exact solution of (5) will be equivalent to the solution of (2), but (5) has one other advantage that, in the first linear approximation to stochastic fluctuations about an equilibrium, or quasi-equilibrium, level, it leads more rapidly to moment or other formulae.

References and short bibliography

ANDREWARTHA, H. G., and BIRCH, L. C. (1954). *The Distribution and Abundance of Animals* (Chicago).

ARMITAGE, P. (1951). 'The statistical theory of bacterial populations subject to mutation', *J. Roy. Statist. Soc.*, B **14**, 1.

ASHBY, E. (1936, 1948). 'Statistical ecology', *Bot. Rev.*, **2**, 221, and **14**, 222.

BACH, P. DE, and SMITH, H. S. (1941). 'Are population oscillations inherent in the host-parasite relation?', *Ecology*, **22**, 363.

BAILEY, N. T. J. (1950). 'A simple stochastic epidemic', *Biometrika*, **37**, 193.

BARTLETT, M. S. (1950). 'Teaching and education in biometry', *Biometrics*, **6**, 85.

BARTLETT, M. S. (1954). 'Processus stochastiques ponctuels', *Ann. Inst. Poincaré*, **14**, fasc. 1, 35.

BARTLETT, M. S. (1955a). *An Introduction to Stochastic Processes* (Cambridge Univ. Press, Cambridge).

BARTLETT, M. S. (1955b). 'The statistical analysis of stochastic processes', *Colloque sur l'analyse statistique (Bruxelles)*.

BARTLETT, M. S. (1956). 'Deterministic and stochastic models for recurrent epidemics', *Proc. Third Berkeley Symposium on Mathematical Statistics and Probability*.

BUSH, R. R., and MOSTELLER, F. (1955). *Stochastic Models for Learning* (Wiley & Sons, New York).

CANE, VIOLET R. (1956). 'Some statistical problems in experimental psychology', *J. Roy. Statist. Soc.*, B (to be published).

CHAPMAN, D. G. (1954). 'The estimation of biological populations', *Ann. Math. Statist.*, **25,** 1.

COCHRAN, W. G. (1950). 'The present status of biometry', *Biometrics*, **6,** 75.

CROW, J., and KIMURA, M. (1956). 'Some genetic problems in natural populations', *Proc. Third Berkeley Symposium on Mathematical Statistics and Probability.*

ELTON, C. S. (1955). 'Natural control of animal populations', Review of Andrewartha and Birch (1954), *Nature*, **176,** 619.

FELLER, W. (1939). 'Die Grundlagen der Volterraschen Theorie des Kampfes ums Dasein in wahrscheinlichkeitstheoretischer Behandlung', *Acta biotheor.*, Leiden, **5,** 11.

FELLER, W. (1940). 'On the logistic law of growth and its empirical verifications in biology', *Acta biotheor.*, Leiden, **5,** 51.

FELLER, W. (1951). 'Diffusion processes in genetics', *Proc. Second Berkeley Symposium on Mathematical Statistics and Probability.*

FINNEY, D. J. (1952). *Statistical Method in Biological Assay* (Griffin & Co., London).

FISHER, R. A. (1925). *Statistical Methods for Research Workers* (Oliver & Boyd, Edinburgh).

FISHER, R. A. (1930). *The Genetical Theory of Natural Selection* (Clarendon Press, Oxford).

FISHER, R. A. (1935). *The Design of Experiments* (Oliver & Boyd, Edinburgh).

GALTON, F. (1888). 'Co-relations and their measurements, chiefly from anthropometric data', *Proc. Roy. Soc.*, **111,** 135.

GALTON, F. (1889). *Natural Inheritance* (London).

GAUSE, G. F. (1934). *The Struggle for Existence* (Baltimore).

GAUSE, G. F. (1935). 'Experimental demonstration of Volterra's periodic oscillations in the numbers of animals', *J. Exp. Biol.*, **12,** 44.

GAUSE, G. F., SMARAGDOVA, N. P., and WITT, A. A. (1936). 'Further studies of interaction between predators and prey', *J. Anim. Ecol.*, **5,** 1.

GRAUNT, JOHN (1662). *Natural and political observations on the bills of mortality* (London).

HALDANE, J. B. S. (1949). 'Some statistical problems arising in genetics', *J. Roy. Statist. Soc.*, B **11**, 1.

HALLEY, E. (1693). 'An estimate of the degrees of the mortality of mankind drawn from curious tables of the births and funerals at the City of Breslaw', *Phil. Trans. Roy. Soc. Lond.*, **17**, 596.

IRWIN, J. O. (1935). 'Some aspects of the development of modern statistical method', *Math. Gaz.*, **19**, 18.

IVERSEN, S., and ARLEY, N. (1950). 'On the mechanism of experimental carcinogenesis', *Act. Path. and Microbiol. Scand.*, **27**, fasc. 5, 773.

KEMPTHORNE, O., *et al.* (editors) (1954). *Statistics and Mathematics in Biology* (Iowa State Coll. Press, Ames, Iowa).

KENDALL, D. G. (1948). 'On the generalized "birth-and-death" process', *Ann. Math. Statist.*, **19**, 1.

KENDALL, D. G. (1954). 'Les processus stochastiques de croissance en Biologie', *Ann. Inst. Poincaré*, **13**, fasc. 1, 53.

KENDALL, D. G. (1956a). 'Deterministic and stochastic epidemics in closed populations', *Proc. Third Berkeley Symposium on Mathematical Statistics and Probability.*

KENDALL, M. G. (1956b). 'Studies in the history of probability and statistics. II. The beginnings of a probability calculus', *Biometrika*, **43**, 1.

KHINTCHINE, A. I. (1949). *Mathematical Foundations of Statistical Mechanics* (translated by G. Gamow; Dover Pub., New York).

KOLMOGOROV, A. (1931). 'Über die analytischen Methoden der Wahrscheinlichkeitsrechnung', *Math. Annalen*, **94**, 415.

KOLMOGOROV, A. (1935). 'Deviations from Hardy's formula in partial isolation', *C.R. Acad. Sci. URSS*, **3**, No. 8, 129.

KOSTITZIN, V. A. (1939). *Mathematical Biology* (Harrap & Co., London).

LESLIE, P. H. (1948). 'Some further notes on the use of matrices in population mathematics', *Biometrika*, **35**, 213.

LI, CHING CHUN (1948). *An Introduction to Population Genetics* (Peking Univ. Press, Peiping).

LOTKA, A. J. (1925). *Elements of Physical Biology* (Williams & Wilkins, Baltimore).

MALÉCOT, G. (1948). *Les mathématiques de l'Hérédité* (Masson et Cie, Paris).

McCULLOCH, W. S., and PITTS, W. (1948). 'The statistical organization of nervous activity', *Biometrics*, **4**, 91.

McKENDRICK, A. G. (1914). 'Studies on the theory of continuous probabilities with special reference to its bearing on natural phenomena of a continuous nature', *Proc. Lond. Math. Soc.*, (2), **13**, 401.

McKENDRICK, A. G. (1926). 'Applications of mathematics to medical problems', *Proc. Edin. Math. Soc.*, **44**, 98.

NEYMAN, J., PARK, T., and SCOTT, E. L. (1956). 'Struggle for existence. The Tribolium model: biological and statistical aspect', *Proc. Third Berkeley Symposium on Mathematical Statistics and Probability*.

ROTHSCHILD, LORD (1953). 'A new method of measuring the activity of spermatozoa', *J. Exp. Biol.*, **30**, 178.

SCHRÖDINGER, E. (1944). 'The statistical law in nature', *Nature*, **153**, 704.

SERFLING, R. E. (1952). 'Historical review of epidemic theory', *Hum. Biol.*, **24**, 145.

TURING, A. M. (1952). 'The chemical basis of morphogenesis', *Phil. Trans. Roy. Soc. Lond.*, Ser. B, **237**, 37.

VOLTERRA, V. (1926). 'Variazioni e fluttuazioni del numero d'individui in specie animali conviventi', *Mem. Acad. Lincei Roma*, **2**, 31.

WALTER, W. GREY (1956). 'The imitation of mentality', *Nature*, **177**, 684.

WRIGHT, S. (1939). 'Statistical genetics in relation to evolution', *Act. Sci. et Ind.*, No. 802 (Herman et Cie, Paris).

WRIGHT, S. (1951). 'The genetical structure of populations', *Ann. Eugen., Lond.*, **15**, 323.

Irreversibility and Statistical Theory

1. *Historical introduction*

Historically the notion of irreversibility has close links with the physical concept of entropy, which is always supposed to increase according to the Second Law of Thermodynamics. In early discussions of statistical mechanics, in which a statistical interpretation of thermodynamics was first attempted, there arose, however, two notorious paradoxes, known as Loschmidt's reversibility paradox (1876) and Zermelo's recurrence paradox (1896). In the first Loschmidt pointed out that from the symmetry of the laws of mechanics with respect to past and future, molecular processes must be reversible, in contradiction to the Second Law. In the second, arguing from a famous theorem in dynamics due to Poincaré (that, under certain conditions about the finiteness of a system's motion, the initial state of the system will recur infinitely often), Zermelo claimed that molecular processes should be cyclical, again in contradiction to the Second Law.

These paradoxes have now been largely resolved, but I think it important to note that only a complete statistical appraisal, first undertaken by Boltzmann, P. and T. Ehrenfest and Smoluchowski, succeeded in achieving this. Moreover, even now further logical consequences of such an appraisal are often overlooked.

Effectively another paradox associated with the Second Law of Thermodynamics was put forward by Maxwell, who invented a demon (known as Maxwell's demon) who sat at the gate between two containers of gas molecules, letting the fast molecules through to one container and stopping the slow ones, thus building-up a higher temperature in one container in contradiction of the Second Law. In a remarkable analysis in 1929, Szilard resolved this paradox by replacing Maxwell's hypothetical demon by a physical device designed to do an equivalent task. He showed, however, that in order to obtain 'information' (in negative entropy measure) of amount I, it was necessary to increase the entropy of the entire system by at least I. Moreover, the maximum reduction in entropy of any subsystem possible by the use of this information was I. Thus the mechanism acted in entire accordance with the Second Law.

Szilard's analysis was remarkable because it preceded modern information and communication theory. Care is necessary in identifying information in this general context too glibly as negative entropy, but I think Szilard's analysis established a close relation or even identity between them in at least the physical example he was discussing. There is of course no peculiarity in the entropy of a subsystem being reduced at the expense of another—refrigerators do this every day; and it is a well-known idea that one fundamental property of living creatures is to extract information or negative entropy from their environment.

However, to come back to the reversibility and recurrence paradoxes, we must define entropy statistically rather carefully, if its increasing nature with time is to be confirmed. Mathematically, if f denotes the complete phase-space distribution of all the molecules of an isolated system, then Liouville's theorem states that the time rate-of-change df/dt is zero. Hence if we attempted to define the entropy S precisely by the standard statistical formula

$$S = -k \int f \log f \, d\tau$$

(where k is a constant, and the integration is over phase-space), then we obtain the trivial result $dS/dt = 0$, or S is constant. I say 'trivial', but this result appears to me to lead to the important but sometimes neglected consequence that if we regard the entire universe as an isolated system and try to associate an absolute time with increasing entropy, then such a time has no meaning for the universe as a whole.*

* See, for example, Bartlett (1950). I see that this point has been made from

In fact, entropy cannot be so defined for an isolated system, but only for a system A connected with another not fully specified system B which creates the disorganization or randomness in A. The system B can and has been envisaged in a wide variety of ways (cf. Moyal, 1949, p. 279).

(i) B may be an external system of which A is merely part. In particular, Boltzmann's 'proof' that entropy increases (his H-theorem) referred merely to a *single* molecule in a gas. The randomness is then due to the interaction of this molecule with the other molecules, akin to the Brownian motion of a particle. In an alternative discussion, Boltzmann included as system B an explicit large system with which A was in thermal contact.

(ii) B may be an internal system of motions ignored in A. Thus Tolman arrived at a general H-theorem by averaging f over small elements of phase-space, the randomness being introduced by the unspecified motion within these elements. The same procedure is adopted in quantum theory by averaging over the phases of the wave-functions. It should be noted that the complete wave-function equation for the entire system A + B is, like equations in classical mechanics, reversible in time (although linear in t, t occurs in the equation as it, and reversing the sign of t is equivalent to reversing the sign of i, and has no consequence in the real world).

With all these devices, the distribution f of the *specified* system A then satisfies the modified kinematic equation

$$df/dt = Rf,$$

where R is an operator depending on the nature of the systems A and B and their interaction. The form of this modified equation does not automatically ensure the tendency of S (as defined above, where integration is now over the retained co-ordinates) to increase with time, but for all physical situations of interest has been found to do so.

With the above interpretation of S, the paradoxes referred to

a slightly different angle by E. A. Milne (1952), who noted Jeans' failure to realize it. Eddington was also sometimes rather lax on this point, as I was too on an earlier occasion (Bartlett, 1936).

have to be modified somewhat. Thus if for definiteness we adopt the viewpoint (ii) and interpret B as an ignored internal system of some kind, then mechanical reversibility, and recurrence in Poincaré's sense, become irrelevant. However, reversibility and recurrence still appear in the *statistical* system A, so that the paradoxes still remain. It is perhaps worth while explaining how these are resolved, making use of the original examples used by the Ehrenfests and by Smoluchowski.

2. *The Ehrenfest and Smoluchowski examples*

In the Ehrenfest model system A consists of two containers enclosing a total of N particles, moving randomly and independently from the first container to the second at an individual average rate λ, and from the second to the first at rate μ. (System B is idealized into the random nature of the motion, and into the ignoring of the motion of individual particles, so that only the numbers n and $n' = N - n$ in the two containers at any time t are of interest.) Mathematically, the evolution of the system can be specified by giving the simultaneous probability $P(n_1, n_2; t_1, t_2)$ of n_1 particles in the first container at time t_1 and n_2 at time t_2, or equivalently, by giving the function

$$\Pi (z_1, z_2) = \Sigma P(n_1, n_2) z_1^{n_1} z_2^{n_2}$$

summed over all possible n_1, n_2. If for convenience we chose our time unit so that $\lambda + \mu = 1$, this latter function may be shown to be (cf. Whittle, 1956)

$$[(\lambda + \mu z_1)(\lambda + \mu z_2) + \lambda \mu e^{-\Delta t} (1 - z_1)(1 - z_2)]^N,$$

where Δt is the difference $| t_2 - t_1 |$; and the complete reversibility in time of the system is immediately apparent. Moreover, the state specified by the number n at time t shows recurrence properties which can be investigated by standard statistical theory (e.g. Bartlett, 1955, § 3.3). Thus the reversibility and recurrence 'paradoxes' still exist for such a system. However, the apparent irreversibility of the process, *starting from any 'non-equilibrium' state*, will manifest itself in an overwhelming tendency (for large N) to move towards states nearer the average, which is, for the first container, $N\mu$. It hardly seems necessary to demonstrate this; it should be sufficient to account for any apparent contradiction by noting that the probabilities now being considered are conditional ones, and not absolute ones (and there may be all the difference in the world between such quantities).

I shall not discuss the concept of entropy in relation to this example, which I am using primarily to explain the notion of statistical reversibility; but I ought perhaps to point out that any formal definition might be somewhat artificial, for entropy is a physical concept (originally introduced only for equilibrium conditions) and the same formula is not necessarily meaningful in all contexts. To explain more technically what I have in mind, it is known (Thomsen, 1953) that Markov chains (of which this is an example) exhibit a tendency to equiprobable states and maximum entropy if the latter is defined as

$$S = - \Sigma_i \, p_i \log p_i \quad \text{(sum over all states)},$$

and the principle of microreversibility holds. We could ensure the latter by putting $\lambda = \mu$ and labelling the particles, but then the idea of tending to a probable state from an initial improbable state would be lost, for all states, defined now in terms of the detailed allocation of the particles between the two containers (rather than of just the numbers of particles in the two containers), would become equally probable. A further discussion of the division of uncertainty between the detailed 'micro-states', and the 'macro-states' specified by the total numbers of particles in the two containers, would be required.†

In terms of these macro-states, any initial state differing markedly from the most probable under equilibrium (stationary) conditions is ultimately very improbable. Nevertheless, the system *will* at some time move back again to the initial state, though the time elapsing before this occurs may be too colossal to contemplate. To illustrate this on a somewhat more realistic example, Smoluchowski showed that for fluctuations in air

[† Cf. Klein, M. J. (1956). 'Entropy and the Ehrenfest urn model', *Physica*, **22**, 569.]

density (at 300° K and 3×10^{19} molecules/c.c.) the mean re-currence time of a 1 per cent fluctuation from the average number for the molecules in a sphere of radius as small as 5×10^{-5} cm. is of order 10^{68} seconds or 3×10^{60} years, far greater than the accepted age of the universe (in so far as the latter has any meaning!). Even Eddington's army of monkeys strumming away at typewriters in the hope of reproducing the whole of English literature might as well give up at the start. However, the time-scale for recurrence is entirely dependent on the scale of the phenomenon considered, and we have only to reduce Smoluchowski's sphere by a factor of 5 in its radius to reduce the mean recurrence time of a 1 per cent fluctuation in density to 10^{-11} seconds. Thus microscopic phenomena have no intrinsic time-direction, at least if this can only be defined in relation to internal entropy increase. This seems an interest-ing point in relation to recent theories of time-reversal in atomic physics, e.g. in the creation and annihilation of positrons and electrons (Margenau, 1954).

A further point about the relation of time with increase of entropy that is stressed in the interesting article by Grünbaum (1955) was argued at some length by the late Hans Reichen-bach. This is, that while in spite of possible ultimate reversi-bility it is legitimate to predict that with increasing time the entropy of a given physical system will increase, this inference is not reciprocal and does not at once allow us to identify in-creasing time with increasing entropy. This is because in the stationary situation of the sort I have just illustrated (omitting for simplicity any difficulties about the statistical definition of entropy for different systems) a time selected at random is just as likely to be one of increasing probability for a rare state (and hence, we shall assume, of decreasing entropy) of a physical system, and hence of no use for defining a time-direction. It is the difference between absolute and conditional probabilities over again. Reichenbach argued that it is necessary to consider an ensemble of 'branch systems' beginning with low entropy, in terms of which the time-direction can be defined in terms of

increasing entropy for the *majority*, with possible deviations for
individual systems. It is possible that the difficulty of an isolated
universe is avoided by the totality of these branch-systems still
being merely part of a larger system; but Reichenbach hardly
solves the problem by this construction, as Grünbaum notes, for
the possibility of such branch-systems being set up depends on
the larger system being in a relatively ordered (low entropy)
configuration. Eddington once made this same point in a charac-
teristically pungent way by remarking that the circumstance
that intelligent human beings were asking these questions indicated that the universe (shall we say the part of the universe
where we are) was in one of its low entropy configurations (thus
ensuring the relevance of conditional probabilities in place of
absolute probabilities). This bears in a curious way on the
question whether we should treat the direction of time as something psychological in relation to which other phenomena
should be considered (as E. A. Milne did), or recognize that
human beings themselves, as well as inanimate matter, are subject to physical laws. I think the latter view must be in one sense
more fundamental; nevertheless, the fact that the human beings
are there has already restricted the physical world they inhabit
to one of a much smaller class than the class of all conceivable
worlds.

If I were to sum up the broad conclusions from my discussion,
it would be that statistical reversibility may impose a lower
limit to the size of systems having any intrinsic time-direction.
At the other end of the scale, the irreversibility of time in terms
of entropy definitions has no meaning for the whole (isolated)
universe, but may have a more local space-time meaning for
comparatively large subsystems, including human beings.

References

BARTLETT, M. S. (1936). 'Intrinsic uncertainty of reference
     frames', *Nature*, **138**, 401.
BARTLETT, M. S. (1950). Discussion on 'Entropy, Time and

Information' by D. M. MacKay, *Report of Proceedings of Symposium on Information Theory* (London), 206.

BARTLETT, M. S. (1955). *An Introduction to Stochastic Processes* (Cambridge).

CHANDRASEKHAR, S. (1943). 'Stochastic problems in physics and astronomy', *Rev. Mod. Physics*, **15**, 1.

EHRENFEST, P. and T. (1907). 'Uber zwei behannte Einwande gegen das Boltzmannsche H-Theorem', *Phys. Zeit.*, **8**, 311.

GRÜNBAUM, A. (1955). 'Time and entropy', *American Scientist*, **43**, 550.

LOSCHMIDT, J. (1876). 'Uber den Zustand des Wärmegleichgewichtes eines Systems von Körpern mit Rücksicht auf die Schwerkraft', *Wien. Ber.*, **73**, I, 128, and II, 366.

MILNE, E. A. (1952). *Sir James Jeans* (Cambridge).

MARGENAU, H. (1954). 'Can time flow backwards?', *Philosophy of Science*, **21**, 79.

MOYAL, J. E. (1949). Discussion following Symposium on Stochastic Processes, *J. Roy. Statist. Soc.*, B **11**, 279.

REICHENBACH, H. (1952–3). 'Les fondements logiques de la mécanique des quanta', *Ann. Inst. Poincaré*, **13**, 109.

ROSENFELD, L. (1955). 'On the foundations of statistical thermodynamics', *Acta Physica Polonica*, **14**, 3.

SMOLUCHOWSKI, M. V. (1915). 'Molekulartheoretische Studien über Umkehr thermodynamisch irreversibler Vorgänge und über Wiederkehr abnormaler Zustände', *Wien. Ber.*, **124**, 339.

SZILARD, L. (1929). 'Über die Entropieverminderung in einem thermodynamischen System bei Eingriffen intelligenter Wesen', *Zeit. f. Phys.*, **53**, 840.

THOMSEN, J. S. (1953). 'Logical relations among the principles of statistical mechanics and thermodynamics', *Phys. Rev.*, **91**, 1263.

WHITTLE, P. (1956). 'Reversibility in Markov processes' (unpublished manuscript).

ZERMELO, E. (1896). 'Ueber einen Satz der Dynamik und die mechanische Wärmetheorie', *Ann. d. Phys.*, **57**, 485.

Statistical Inference

The permanent and essential place of statistical concepts in science is one that few would query. The problem that the statistician is continually facing of how to draw conclusions from statistical observations is, however, one that still arouses considerable controversy. On reflection this is less surprising than it might seem at first. In branches of science more specifically related to tangible things, the scientist is usually able to work away quite happily with his mathematical formulae or laboratory apparatus or field observations without worrying unduly about the philosophical foundations of science itself. Even if he is aware that there is a general problem of inductive inference, of how and with what justification he is able to draw any conclusions from his observations that will extend beyond the observations themselves, he does not find this problem interfering very extensively with his day-to-day work. Often he has a fairly good theory already available on which to fit his further calculations or observations, for example, Newtonian mechanics for the astronomer predicting an eclipse of the sun, or quantum mechanics for the physicist studying atomic spectra. The question of how far these theories are applicable is one that can, if considered at all, be considered separately; the immediate task is one that may involve a series of calculations and observations over a protracted period, requiring considerable concentration and no disturbing interference from philosophers or logicians who might undermine the scientist's faith in what he is doing.

The difficulty with the work of a statistician, at least one involved in scientific research, is that his work has usually arisen in fields, for example, in agriculture or in psychology, where attempts to explain the data have to be more limited in aim, because no complete theory, at least of a tractable kind, exists that will eliminate the need for much interim work of a more empirical character. This means that the statistician is often concerned with what we might term 'little inductions', some comparatively modest conclusions that nevertheless contribute to quantitative progress in the field of application to which his data belong. It should be emphasized that there is no hard-and-fast division between the statistician and other scientists, with whom of course he often co-operates; nevertheless, this continual encounter with the inference problem makes him pay rather more attention to it than many of his scientific colleagues need to do. Perhaps this explains why it is that discussions on scientific inference in general often devote considerable space to the problem of statistical inference. This in my view is a little dangerous. Certainly before we can consider statistical inference we need to consider what its subject-matter is, and how statistical inference is to be distinguished from scientific inference in general. This is not always done; in fact, by the use of the same probability concept for the lesser and greater problem the distinction has sometimes been slurred over.

Let me therefore make it clear that by statistical data and statistical phenomena I refer to numerical and quantitative facts about groups or classes of individuals or events, rather than facts about the individuals themselves. If for the purpose of a statistical survey I classify an individual according to his height (or income) and put him in a group with all the other individuals having the same height (or income), it does not mean that I deny the importance and interest of other attributes of that individual, whether he is fat or cheerful or a bachelor; it is merely that they are not thought to be immediately relevant to my particular enquiry, and are ignored. Sometimes on the grounds of expediency one is obliged to ignore possibly relevant facts, as when the results of a clinical trial of some drug are assessed statistically without the individual characteristics of each patient being explored to the full. This example perhaps brings out both the essential nature of the statistical approach and its consequent limitations.

9

Now we can try to see what is meant by statistical inference. It is inference from statistical data, and makes use of its own intrinsic theoretical concepts associated with the regularity properties of statistical groups and populations, and formulated mathematically in terms of the theory of probability. There is no doubt about the existence of these regularity properties. If you query this, pour a lot of marbles through a funnel in the top-centre of a bagatelle board containing the usual collection of nails, and observe the smooth pattern or distribution of marbles collecting in the various compartments at the bottom of the board. What might and has been questioned is the abstraction of the concept of statistical probability, obeying definite quantitative laws, from such observed phenomena. This is admittedly a theoretical procedure which has no more (and no less) logical justification than the use of concepts in other scientific contexts; but I am not primarily concerned here with the justification of scientific induction in general, but to explain what statistical inference is about, and I do not want to confuse the two. It is quite natural in this statistical context to consider the relative proportions of different kinds of event (different compartments for the marbles), and to postulate, because these observed proportions are found to stabilize as the total number of events (marbles) increases, ideal fractions or proportions p_r in our associated conceptual model, such that the addition law for mutually exclusive events (different compartments) holds when we consider the proportion for one or other of two events (compartments). The other probability law, that of multiplication, is merely a definition of conditional probability, i.e. the relative proportion in a restricted class of events (for example, the proportion of marbles in one compartment when we restrict our attention to the total number of marbles falling into, say, two compartments of which this is one).

I have already mentioned the use by some logicians of probability in the wider context of inductive inference, where it is introduced as a degree of belief or credibility. Some think of it in connection with personal assessments of degrees of belief and others claim that it can be given a more absolute interpretation, but they will agree that it is something different from the concept of statistical probability as such.

The American logician Rudolf Carnap introduced the notation p_1 and p_2 for credibility and statistical probability respectively, but I prefer to use my own earlier suggestion of P for the former and p for the latter. It is plausible to ascribe the same rules for these probabilities P as for p, but it should be noticed that this is partly a convention, in that the addition law for p is taken over in order to maintain general consistency. The rules for P do not represent any theory about particular kinds of phenomena, but are, as Sir Harold Jeffreys puts it, epistemological in character and are intended to be used for all phenomena, indeed for all possible propositions about phenomena we may choose to make. The proposal by writers such as Jeffreys that we should explicitly make use of probability theory in this wider P sense every time we make an induction is not one that is generally accepted, and I for one consider that it usually obscures more issues than it resolves. One is free to choose what procedures one likes as long as one is able to attain some measure of general acceptance of them and some success with them. Those who like to make explicit use of degrees of belief or credibility are not prevented; on the other hand those of us who think this is liable to confuse by spurious over-simplification and who prefer to make their final inductions in a less formal manner, though making use of any interim deductions, including where relevant calculations (routine or otherwise) of a statistical nature, should not be attacked as logically incompetent.

The appearance of both kinds of probability P and p in one logical relation can be exemplified by writing down in P symbols what is equivalent to Bayes's theorem of inverse probability, by means of which inference from effect to cause has been formalized. Let us denote the probability P of a proposition A on data B by $P(A \mid B)$. Then, if some data S are considered on two alternative hypotheses H_1 and H_2, we write formally, according to the usual rules of probability,

$$P(H_1 \mid S)P(S) = P(H_1, S) = P(H_1)P(S \mid H_1),$$
$$P(H_2 \mid S)P(S) = P(H_2, S) = P(H_2)P(S \mid H_2),$$

whence

$$\frac{P(H_1 \mid S)}{P(H_2 \mid S)} = \frac{P(H_1)}{P(H_2)} \frac{P(S \mid H_1)}{P(S \mid H_2)}. \tag{1}$$

In words, the relative odds of the two hypotheses after the data S are available are equal to the product of the prior odds, before S are available, and the probability ratio of S on H_1 and H_2. The relation (1) is, if the P symbolism is accepted, quite general, and has nothing to do with statistical inference as such. However, if the hypothesis H_1 or H_2 and the data S are statistical in character, so that there is an acceptable statistical probability $p(S \mid H_1)$ or $p(S \mid H_2)$, it is natural to equate $P(S \mid H_1)/P(S \mid H_2)$ with $p(S \mid H_1)/p(S \mid H_2)$, so that relation (1) then reads

$$\frac{P(H_1 \mid S)}{P(H_2 \mid S)} = \frac{P(H_1)}{P(H_2)} \frac{p(S \mid H_1)}{p(S \mid H_2)}. \tag{2}$$

Note that the probability ratio $p(S \mid H_1)/p(S \mid H_2)$ (or the likelihood ratio as it is sometimes called when the change of $p(S \mid H)$ with H rather than with S is under discussion) is the only quantity on the right that involves the data S, so that this formalism does suggest the relevant function of S to consider in any inference about H.

Objections to the use of (2) begin to arise if we are tempted to insert values for the prior odds $P(H_1)/P(H_2)$, for these (except in a few special statistical problems) involve P, not p, quantities and it is not clear that any useful purpose is served in inserting values that are not necessarily accepted by others. A typical criticism of the assessment of P probabilities is contained in the following passage* of the late Sir Arthur Eddington:

> One difficulty in employing strength of belief as a measure of probability is that an expectation or belief has partly a subjective basis. We have agreed that it depends

[* Cf. the somewhat more abbreviated quotation of this passage in the first essay.]

(and ought to depend) on the information or evidence supplied; but in addition the strength of the expectation depends on the personality of the man who weighs the evidence. We try to remove this subjective element by saying that the true probability corresponds to the judgment of a 'right-thinking person'; but how shall we define this ideal referee? We do not mean a perfectly logical person, for there is no question of making a strictly logical deduction from the evidence; if that were possible the conclusion would be a matter of certainty not probability. We do not mean a person gifted with second-sight, for we want to know the probability relative to the information stated and not relative to occult information. We do not particularly mean a person of long experience in similar judgments, for he is likely to use his past experience to supplement surreptitiously the information on which the judgment of probability is ostensibly based. Apart from the obvious definition of a right-thinking person as 'someone who thinks as I do' (wnich is probably the definition at the back of our minds) there seems to be no way of defining his qualities (*New Pathways in Science*, p. 112).

The very notion of the probability of a hypothesis is of course a controversial one, for people would differ in their attitude to the question whether to talk of the truth or falsehood of scientific hypotheses has a meaning. For this sort of reason, statisticians usually prefer to concentrate on $p(S \mid H)$ or $p(S \mid H_1)/p(S \mid H_2)$, i.e. on statistical probabilities and associated quantities; they feel they are most qualified to deal with these, just as a chemist would concentrate on chemical concepts or a physicist on physical concepts. This of course is in situations where a precise probability specification of the data in a statistical sense is feasible. It has sometimes been claimed by mathematical statisticians that this kind of statistical inference is all they should be concerned with, but most statisticians are aware of other situations where conclusions are perforce less precise because the data, while statistical, do not permit any precise probability specification or model to be set up.

The technical details of statistical methodology hardly need be gone into here, as I am not claiming that they represent final conclusions in any problem, but merely statistical transformations and reductions of the evidence that assist in its interpretation and understanding. Many problems that present themselves are of fairly routine type for which standardized statistical techniques have been developed and can be applied. Rather analogously to the use of techniques in the experimental sciences or in mathematics, this saves the statistician much time and thought whenever he has to analyse data. However, it seems to me important that those who use these more routine methodological procedures should bear in mind not only Mach's dictum of science as an economy of thought, but also the criticism of this dictum that this should not imply that scientists need not think! No scientific procedures, statistical or otherwise, should be allowed to become too mechanical. One practical quality that the statistician has often seemed to acquire, through his continual encounter with all kinds of data and the problem of their collection and interpretation, is a capacity to appraise the general logical milieu surrounding a particular task, so that he has been able to advise on the planning of surveys, the design of experiments, and on other matters relating to the purpose and conduct of investigations. Unlike the pure mathematician or the research chemist, the statistician cannot select for study component parts of a problem or of observational material, or he may disturb the probabilities and averages it is his job to assess. He has to learn to see a problem or a set of data as a whole. Such an ability is of course extremely useful in day-to-day, as well as in scientific, affairs.

References and further bibliography

BARTLETT, M. S. (1933). 'Probability and chance in the theory of statistics', *Proc. Roy. Soc. A*, **141**, 518.

BARTLETT, M. S. (1949). 'Probability in logic, mathematics and science', *Dialectica*, **3**, 104.

BRAITHWAITE, R. B. (1953). *Scientific Explanation* (Cambridge).

CARNAP, R. (1944-5). 'The two concepts of probability', *Philosophy and Phenomenological Research*, **5**, 513.

EDDINGTON, A. (1935). *New Pathways in Science* (Cambridge).

FISHER, R. A. (1956). *Statistical Methods and Scientific Inference* (Oliver & Boyd, Edinburgh).

GOOD, I. J. (1950). *Principles of Probability and of Weighing Evidence* (Griffin, London).

HARROD, R. F. (1956). *Foundations of Inductive Logic* (Macmillan, London).

JEFFREYS, H. (1957). *Scientific Inference* (2nd ed., Cambridge).

RAMSEY, F. P. (1931). *The Foundations of Mathematics and other Logical Essays* (London).

SAVAGE, L. J. (1954). *Foundations of Statistics* (Wiley, New York).

Appendix

The more sophisticated reader will doubtless feel somewhat dissatisfied with the above remarks, either on the grounds that the orthodox techniques used in statistical analysis are not explicitly described or because insufficient indication is given that these are still as much as ever in debate. In answer I would first point out the introductory nature of the talk which these written comments summarize, and suggest that the popular practice of making completely condemnatory remarks at the expense of followers of schools of thought to which one does not personally belong is likely merely to bewilder the beginner, who may reasonably conclude that if so many illustrious thinkers can commit so many howlers he had better abandon at once his own diffident excursion into so prickly a field.

At the same time there is perhaps some obligation in this printed record to clarify my apparently rather non-committal attitude further, especially in view of recent publications such as the books by Savage, Fisher and Harrod included in the bibliography, or the even more recent book by Lancelot Hogben on *Statistical Theory* in which present controversies are construed as a crisis in statistical theory.*

A topic discussed in detail by Savage that has received much attention in recent years, particularly in America, is 'decision theory', and the use of 'utilities' as well as prior probabilities to appraise the relative values of different possible actions or 'strategies'. Such analysis seems to me an important addition to the type of analysis represented by Bayes's theorem and inverse

* Subsequent note. The reader is recommended to read also other opinions and reviews before arriving at his own final judgment. Attention is especially drawn to the reviews of the books by Savage and Fisher by van Dantzig (1957), to a review of Hogben's book by Lindley (1958), who in this review is much more sympathetic to Savage's book than van Dantzig, and to my review of Fisher's book. Note should also be made of a conference on Statistical Inference held in London in July 1959, at which various opinions and views currently held were clearly brought out.

probability, but does not differ in kind from it; and the practice of many statisticians, including myself, of avoiding explicit use of such analysis in scientific discussion of statistical problems is therefore not greatly affected.

To come to Hogben's book, I certainly think Hogben too sweeping in his attack on some of the current methods of statistics; for example, where he suggests that in place of blind adherence to 'cookery-books' of statistical method, 'laboratory experiments will have to stand on their own feet without protection from a façade of irrelevant computations' (p. 30). It is misleading to imply that research workers will automatically be better without the discipline which the statistical design and analysis of experiment has imposed on them. It is the experience of many statisticians asked to advise on experimental or other investigations that the purpose of the work is obscure, and logical clarification is at such a stage often more important than detailed procedures. The latter, however, like scientific apparatus, are available ready-to-hand, and the fact that they are sometimes less immediately or perfectly relevant than others is no excuse for their outright rejection, and for the consequent saddling of the unfortunate investigator with the impracticable task of devising new and *ah hoc* methods for every piece of research that he undertakes.

Nevertheless, Hogben's attitude elsewhere has much in common with my own. Thus he criticizes 'a monistic prejudice which demands a unitary formula for scientific method' (p. 472), and couples the value of *statistical* theory and method closely with the properties of averages and aggregates, and to situations where observed frequencies can be used in support of theoretical probabilistic or statistical concepts.

Perhaps the chief specific topic that requires further commentary concerns the place and status of fiducial probability (in the sense of R. A. Fisher) and confidence intervals (in the sense of J. Neyman), because these concepts have appeared in appropriate contexts as rivals to inverse probability methods, and are to some extent rival concepts to each other; they are also related to an inductive method put forward in Harrod's book. The method of confidence intervals is merely one of the routine statistical techniques of estimation available in statistical situations where a precise probability specification of the sampling variability is available, and in my opinion should be regarded as such. Its logical interest resides in its apparent by-passing of the inductive problem by two simultaneous devices: (i) making a statement whose probability of truth is known quantitatively, provided the statement is regarded as one of many such, and the sample in question is not elevated to a unique position (the inference is thus essentially a statistical one and must be so interpreted); (ii) basing the precision of the statement on the probability specification, which consequently has to be correct, and while sometimes it will be general enough to be acceptable, its acceptance represents the overlooked induction without which (i) is meaningless. An example may make this clearer. Suppose no lamps, when a sample of 50 was taken, have given a test-life of less than 1,800 hours. How many can be expected to give as short a life in a further batch of 50? An inference, based on the exact probabilities of getting the observed number of faulty lamps, or less, in a sample of 50, given the total finite population of 100 and the total (unknown) number of failures in this population, is that the number will be not greater than 5. The probability of this assertion is not less than 0·95, in the sense that inferences based on the rule indicated will be correct at least in this proportion of cases (the 'at least' is not important, arising from the discrete nature of the population, and removable, if desired, by an auxiliary sampling device).

The essential induction here, even after the statistical nature of the assertion has been agreed on, is that the actual sample was a random sample from the total batch of 100. This specification is here at its simplest, and could hardly be any less. *It cannot (in this context) be dispensed with.*

Some of the differences between the theories of fiducial probability and of confidence intervals are too technical to be gone into here (for some further comments see my review of

Fisher's book), but in recent years it has become clear that Fisher rejects the frequency interpretation of fiducial probability, and for this reason I consider that fiducial probability (if it can be made internally consistent) comes logically in the same class as inverse probability, in the sense that the probabilities it uses are in general not of the p class (or Carnap's p_2) referred to earlier.

The inverse probability statement in the above example would be, *on the basis that the possible values for the unknown proportion of failures are all equally likely* (in the P, or Carnap's p_1, sense), that the probability of 5 or fewer is 0·987. The statement appears more powerful than the earlier one. One reason is the discrete nature of the distributions in this example, so that the 0·95 confidence probability does not coincide with the sum of the probability ordinates (which come to 0·972). The other reason, however, arises from the prior probability distribution, which if available in the frequency sense would have been used without question by any statistician. It is the fact that it is not available in this sense that makes its use different in kind from the hypothesis of a random sample in the confidence interval inference.

In his book Harrod makes use of the same sort of device that is used in the theory of confidence intervals. To make the relation more apparent, consider first a fairly well-known conundrum of a man entering a strange town and seeing a tram with number x. What can he say about the town's total number of trams? On the assumption (*not* so acceptable in this context) that this number is a random selection from the set 1 to N, where N is unknown, the probability of x or less is x/N. Choosing n such that $x/n \geqslant p$, we assert that $N \geqslant n$ with a confidence greater than or equal to p.

Harrod applies this kind of argument to the total length L of a journey, making the interesting point that no assumption of randomness is here needed. A traveller cannot make an inference about L after any chosen distance travelled x (without an assumption about probable lengths of journeys in the P

sense). However, if he considers making inferences about L at *all stages of his journey*, the one made, say, at distance x being that this length L is not less than x/p, then these inferences will be correct in the proportion p of cases. The logical interest here is that the 'ergodic' requirement of sampling all distances x in L uniformly is satisfied automatically, and does not have to rely on the randomness postulate. Of course anyone who has secret information about L will know that the inferences will at first all be correct, and suddenly become erroneous when the distance L has been traversed, but this does not invalidate the entire set of inferences made, though it may make it less relevant once the journey has started.†

Further references

BARTLETT, M. S. (1937). 'Subsampling for attributes', *J. Roy. Statist. Soc. (Suppl.)*, **4**, 131.

BARTLETT, M. S. (1957). Review of R. A. Fisher's book: 'Statistical Methods and Scientific Inference', *Biometrika*, **44**, 293.

HOGBEN, L. (1957). *Statistical Theory* (Allen & Unwin Ltd, London).

LINDLEY, D. V. (1958). 'Professor Hogben's "crisis"—a survey of the foundations of statistics', *Applied Statistics*, **7**, 186.

VAN DANTZIG, D. (1957). 'Statistical priesthood (Savage on personal probabilities)', *Statistica Neerlandica*, **11**, 1.

VAN DANTZIG, D. (1957). 'Statistical priesthood II (Sir Ronald on scientific inference)', *Statistica Neerlandica*, **11**, 185.

† Harrod attempts to meet this last difficulty by a further discussion and modification of the set of inferences, but I do not follow or accept his further argument, which is consequently not referred to here.

Index of Names

(where included in the text)

INDEX OF NAMES

INDEX OF NAMES